Best Wishes

Rama Setu
Symbol of National Unity

RAMA SETU
SYMBOL OF NATIONAL UNITY

Subramanian Swamy

Former Union Law Minister, Government of India
Former Professor of Economics, IIT Delhi and
Faculty of Harvard University

HAR-ANAND
PUBLICATIONS PVT LTD

HAR-ANAND PUBLICATIONS PVT LTD

E-49/3, Okhla Industrial Area, Phase-II, New Delhi-110020
Tel.: 41603490 Fax: 011-41708607
E-mail: haranand@rediffmail.com
Website: www.haranandpublications.com

Published by Ashok Gosain and Ashish Gosain for
Har-Anand Publications Pvt Ltd

Printed in India at Ram Book Binding House

Preface

The Rama Setu is a wonderful historical causeway that physically separates the turbulent Bay of Bengal in the north from the calm and tranquil waters of Gulf of Mannar in the south, while spiritually and emotionally uniting the South with North India. The 1.5 to 2.5 m thick zone of coral and rock presently occurring at shallow depths in the sea atop the crustal portion of the Rama Setu appears to be an ancient causeway as vividly described in Valmiki's *Ramayana*. The ancient architects appear to have taken advantage of the crustal portion of the ridge to minimize dumping of large volume of rocks and boulders and also utilized less dense but compact rocks and boulders so that these could be carried easily to greater distances and at the same time strong enough to withstand pressure from above both by human as well as sea forces. Due to the tranquil condition, very rare species of corals and other sea organisms grew in the Gulf of Mannar, whereas the species are completely absent in the turbulent Bay of Bengal side. The choppy tide and the associated sediments caused by severe cyclones that occur every year in the Bay of Bengal are prevented by the ridge of the Rama Setu and thereby protect the delicate conditions in the Gulf of Mannar. So too we find now from the researches of scientists, that even Tsunami was moderated by the existence of the Rama Setu. Otherwise, there would have been a funneling effect, causing enormous damage several times over than what was experienced.

The Tamil Nadu Chief Minister Mr Karunanidhi and his lieutenant, the Union Shipping & Road Transport Minister Mr TR Baalu, have been telling outright lies to the public about the non-existence of the Rama Setu, and on the economic and environmental viability of the Sethusamudram Shipping Channel Project (SSCP).

The Ministry of Environment & Forests in fact, in a letter dated April 8, 1999 to the Ministry of Surface Transport, had conveyed it's opinion that the SSCP should be scrapped as it would be an environmental disaster. This opinion was based on an analysis of the NEERI Report of 1998. Yet in 2004 the Ministry reversed it's opinion based on the same 1998 data. Why? No explanation has been given so far for this somersault.

The Minister has also suppressed from public view a report prepared by Dr S Badrinarayanan, former Director of Geological Survey of India (GSI) in which, based on a 2002 investigation under the sea near and at the Setu, concluded that Rama Setu had been constructed, at least 9000 years ago, and that it is *not* a natural formation as claimed by the Tamil Nadu Chief Minister Mr Karunanidhi and his followers. However, without consulting the GSI, the Union Government hastily filed an affidavit in the Supreme Court in a Writ Petition filed by this author, to aver that "there is no information or studies in the knowledge of the Government that Rama Setu in man made". Former ASI DG SR Rao has also ridiculed this stand of the government.

The Government's decision to implement the SSCP is vitiated by arbitrariness, unreasonableness, and sheer anti-Hindu bias of the decision-makers. Hence it cannot stand scrutiny in court. At present, the Supreme Court has stayed the demolition of the Rama Setu on my *prima facie* valid arguments in Court. The SSCP is also an economic loss, an environmental disaster, a national security risk, and of monumental corruption. It will enable dredging companies to make easy money and help LTTE to move it's terrorist and narcotic base to Kerala Coast. Therefore, this anti-national project should be scrapped, if no other alternative route, without breaking Rama Setu, is not acceptable to the Government.

Hence, to establish the truth and defend the Rama Setu, I thought I should not only approach the Courts to put the Government to strict proof, but write a book to document, in simplified language to the extent possible, the facts about the whole matter and thus inform the public.

In writing this book, I have been benefited by the earlier researches of several writers in the field such as Capt H Balakrishnan, Dr S Kalyanaraman, and V. Sundaram, IAS (Retd). Ms VS Chandralekha IAS (Retd), and my party colleague, deserves special thanks for providing me useful insights and also urging me to take interest in the campaign against the project as it is currently designed.

My wife, Dr Roxna S. Swamy, Advocate, Supreme Court, took pains to assist me in editing the materials and correcting the facts in the book. She also visited Rama Setu and climbed on it, to inform others that the causeway did indeed exist and can be seen. She is owed my heartfelt thanks, without of course holding her responsible for the remaining errors in the book.

My grateful thanks are also due to Ms Subbulakshmi who patiently typed several drafts of the manuscripts without complaining.

SUBRAMANIAN SWAMY

Contents

CHAPTER 1

Introduction

On July 2 2005, Prime Minister Manmohan Singh pressed a button in Madurai to signify the commencement of work on the much publicized Sethusamudram Ship Channel Project (SSCP) costing the public Rs. 2427.40 crores (see Box 1). Why he did it in Madurai and not in Rameshwaram is a mystery.

This ambitious and technologically challenging project attempts to create a long offshore navigation channel linking the Gulf of Mannar with the Bay of Bengal through the Rama Setu. Its proponents have christened it as "India's Suez Canal". Of course, there is a difference: Suez Canal is a land based ship channel, while the Sethusamudram Ship Channel is a furrow through the sea floor.

Technical feasibility of digging such a channel, was never much in doubt, but the financial viability of the project was always doubted. Hence despite the recommendation of several expert committees, the project had hitherto remained on paper giving rise to speculation that no government was inclined to implement the project.

Because the waters called Palk Straits between India and Sri Lanka are too shallow for navigation, India today does not have, within her own territorial waters, a continuous navigable route around the Indian peninsula (which has a coastline 7517 kms. long). Hence, the search for furrowing out a channel through the straits. Moreover all ships traveling from the west coast of India to the east coast of of India (and especially those traveling eastward from Tuticorin Port), have to go round Sri Lanka, entailing an additional distance of hundreds of kilometers, and extra hours of sailing time.

Government of India
Ministry of Shipping, Road Transport & Highway
Department of Shipping
Transport Bhavan, 1, Parliament Street
New Delhi

No PD-26014/3/2004-Sethu   Dated the 1st June 2005

To

The Chairman-Cum Managing Director,
Sethusamudram Corporation Limited
Tuticorin Port Trust,
Tuticorin

Subject : Implementation of Sethusamudram Ship Channel Project (SSCP)

Sir,

I am directed to convey the sanction of the competent authority for implementation of Sethusamudram Ship Channel Project at a cost of Rs. 2427.40 Crores consisting of capital cost of Rs. 2233 Crores and financing cost of Rs. 194.40 Crores including interest During Construction (IDC) component of Rs. 126.80 Crores, subject to the following conditions:

M/s Sethusamudram Corporation Limited (SCL) will be the nodal agency for raising resources and implementing the project through Tuticorin Port Trust.

The financial structure of the M/s SCL will be as under, keeping the debt equity ratio as 1.5 : 1

Total Project cost	: Rs. 2427.40 Crores
Equity	: Rs. 971.00 Crores
Debt (About 50% in domestic currency and the balance in foreign exchange)	: Rs. 1456.40 Crores

The equity contribution of Rs. 971 crores in M/s SCL by different agencies shall be as under:

S. No.	Name of the Organisation	Equity Contribution (Rs. in Crores)
1	Government of India	495
2	Tuticorin Port Trust	50
3	Shipping Corporation of India	50
4	Dredging Corporation of India	30
5	Chennai Port Trust	30
6	Ennore Port Limited	30
7	Visakhapatnam Port Trust	30
8	Paradip Port Trust	30
9	IPO/Private Placement/Users	226

1. Government of India's guarantee shall be extended for domestic an foreign debt to be raised for his project.

2. The principle approval is also accorded to provide interest free non-plan loan assistance of Rs. 390.05 Crores from the Government of India and Rs. 374.75 Crores from the other Ports and PSUs that are equity partners in the SPV in proportion to their equity holding for offsetting the negative cash flow, over a period of first 9 years of operation starting from the year 2009-2010.

3. Approval is also accorded for awarding redging work in a stretch of the channel involving 12 to 13 million cubic meters of dredging in Palk Strait area adjoining Bay of Bengal, to the Dredging Corporation of India (DCI) on nomination basis subject to DC I guaranteeing completion of the work as per agreed schedule. The rates payable to DCI for this work will be the prevailing market rates.

Yours faithfully

Sd/-

(S.K. Shahi)

Under Secretary to the Government of India

Besides the shallowness of the Palk Strait, there is also a barrier that is partly natural (i.e., Pamban Island) and partly an ancient monument (i.e., Rama Setu) which together span the straits from the Indian coast to Sri Lanka, viz., from Mandapam to Talaimanar. Hence for long it has been proposed that the straits be dredged and the spanning formation be cut through for a navigable channel.

Thus the proposal for providing a navigable route, termed "Alignment", has been attracting the attention of the Government of India for a long time. The first proposal was initiated in 1860; and since then between 1860 and 1922, as many as nine committees have been set up for dredging a channel. But because of the sheer economics of the project, the idea of a dredged channel was dropped each time.

After independence, five committees have been set up for the Sethusamudram Ship Canal Project at different times; the most recent one (1997) was S. Gopalan's Steering Group [see Figure 2]. The proposals of these committees were dropped for reasons of economics and environment.

In 1997, based on a Report of the National Environmental Engineering Research Institute (NEERI), Nagpur (a CSIR institution), the Union Ministry of Environment and Forests had first chosen a channel alignment through Pambam Island; but in 1999 the same Ministry somersaulted by recommending that the Ministry of Surface Transport dump the project altogether (see Annexure 5). In 2002, it again somersaulted and chose the present Alignment No. 6 that proposes a cut through the Rama Setu for the channel.

The project, as now envisaged, requires the channel to run parallel and proximate to the Indo-Sri Lankan maritime boundary. The channel claim is that by avoiding the often turbulent passage around Sri Lanka, there is a saving of up to 424 nautical miles (780 kms) and up to 30 hours in sailing time. The channel will have a length of 167.22 km with two dredged channels - the first across the Rama Setu (and which, as will become apparent, is not really a dredging operation at all, but rather is a digging and blasting operation) and the second through the shallows of Palk Bay where the Palk Strait will be deepened. The length of these dredged channels will be 35 km and 54 km respectively. Palk Bay in between the two dredged channels will have adequate natural depth (for the proposed channel design) and does not require any dredging. The Project envisages more than 82 million cubic meters of dredging, which dredging alone accounts for 77 per cent of the Project cost.

It is estimated that in 2008, the first year of operation, 3,055 ships will transit through the channel, translating into the above nine transits of cargo ships per day. It is estimated that two years later, 7141 ships will choose to transit through the channel. In view of environmental sensitivity, crude oil carriers would however not be allowed through the channel in laden condition.

It is also estimated that per annum 1.5 to 2 million cubic metres of maintenance dredging would be required for the channel because sea tides will keep dumping sand in the furrow that has been dug out. Dumping sites have been identified in the project in such a way that the dumped materials will not move either in the direction of the Indian and Sri Lankan coasts, or towards the channel. Dumping of dredged materials in any location other than the pre-chosen sites has been prohibited.

The Sethusamudram Corporation Ltd. (SCL), the Special Purpose Vehicle created by the Central Government for the financing and execution of the project, was registered as a company in 2005, with a complement of only 30 officers and staff: not many officers in the port sector have been willing to join, perhaps overawed by the rigorous demands of the project in the execution phase.

A project of the size and nature of Sethusamudram Project should, it is assumed, lead to infrastructural and economic development in the Project area. With a view to acting as a catalyst, SCL has proposed a coastal community development program with an outlay of Rs. 60 crore, most of which is earmarked for development of a minor port at Rameshwaram and at least four fishing harbours. But it may be mentioned that the International Shipping Association has ruled out any fishing or fishing crafts once the channel becomes operational. This has been kept secret from the fishermen.

On December 11, 2006, to enable completion of the whole project by November 2008, (the target date for commissioning the channel), the Union Minister of Shipping inaugurated the dredging project off Rameshwaram,. The daunting task of completing the dredging project, is vested solely in the Dredging Corporation Ltd (the DCI)., which is undertaking a capital dredging project of this magnitude for the first time since its inception. This itself puts a question mark on the project since DCI lacks the necessary equipment for dredging on the sea floor. The one dredger it had, has already been completely damaged in January 2007 when it tried to dredge through the Rama Setu.

A perusal of the history of the Project reveals that ever since 1860 when, for the first time it was mooted to form a continuous navigable route connecting the Gulf of Mannar with the Palk Bay, different channel alignments or directions were identified by different expert committees. Between 1860 and 1922, all the nine committees made proposals that envisaged cutting through the Pambam Island and not through the Rama Setu. But none of them materialized or fructified for want of financial resources.

After Independence, authorities considered several Channel alignments before the Government finally chose (in 2004), the present Alignment No. 6 and launched the project in July 2005. Under the present scheme of things, the channel's total length will be about 167 km. It will be 35 km long in the Rama Setu area; 54 km in the Palk Strait, and 78 km in the Palk Bay. As stated earlier, no dredging is required in the Palk Bay as it already has enough natural depth, of over 20 metres.

In the mid-1950s, the Union government had constituted the Ramaswami Mudaliar Committee, whose suggested channel alignment (proposed in 1961) was the first in the post-Independence period. According to this Alignment, a crossing through the mainland at Mandappam was recommended, *and specifically it was recommended not to touch the Rama Setu.* In 1968, the Venkateswaran Committee suggested an Alignment which would cut across Pamban Island near the Rameshwaram area But neither of these alignments was pursued by the Government.

In 1981, one more Alignment, cutting across near Dhanushkodi west of the Kothandaramaswamy temple, was proposed by the Lakshminarayanan Committee. Till this time, the major factor influencing the final recommendation for the Project was economic viability with apparently no consideration to the environmental/ ecological aspects. According to the comprehensive environmental impact assessment report prepared in August 2004 by the National Environmental Engineering Research Institute (NEERI), those were the days when, even at the national level, environmental aspects of development projects were rarely addressed.

In 1996, the newly elected DMK Tamil Nadu State Government got the 1981 proposal updated for economic viability by the Pallavan Transport Corporation, and it sought approval from the Union Government headed by Prime Minister Deve Gowda.

A Steering Committee of the Union Shipping Ministry was then appointed in 1997 which suggested that the Dhanushkodi portion of the alignment, popularly called the Alignment No. 4, be located east of the temple. In 1998, yet another Alignment was proposed by the NEERI. The channel or alignment proposed was the same as Alignment No. 4, but instead of cutting through Rameshwaram Island, it went around Dhanushkodi. A year later this proposal was rejected on environmental and navigational grounds, because it would have required blasting the coral reefs east of Dhanushkodi.

The present (and sixth) channel alignment (or Alignment No. 6) was suggested by the NEERI in its initial environmental examination (EIA) in 2002 (see Annexure 2). This would cut through the holy Rama Setu. This is the first ever Alignment proposal that called for cutting through the Rama Setu.

All six Alignments proposed since 1860, are summarized in Table 1 and traced in Figure 2 below. Interestingly, the latest EIA report (of August 2004) of NEERI does not give any reasons for abandoning Alignment No. 4 in favour of Alignment No. 6 (see Annexure 3). Nor is any explanation provided as to why the NEERI and the Ministry of Environment & Forest somersaulted from the position taken in 1999 in a letter to the Ministry of Surface Transport, that SSCP "not be taken up at all" (Annexure 5). No new data had been collected to warrant a review.

Table 1 **Various proposals since 1860 for a Sethusamudram Channel Based on Counter Affidavit filed by Union of India in the Supreme Court of India in transfer Petition No. 26/27 of 2007 of Subramanian Swamy vs Union of India**

S. No.	Report	Year	Recommendation
I.	Before Independence in 1947		
1.	Cmdr Taylor's (Indian Marine Corp	1860	Cut through 12 miles (19.2 kms) West of Pamban i.e., through land area on main coasline in Tamil Nadu (Alignment No. 1)
2.	Mr. Townsend's	1861	Deepen existing Pamban Channel i.e. through the sea between Tamil Nadu's coastline and Rameshwaram Island (Modified Alignment No. 1)

3.	H.M. Government's (Parliamentary Committee's)	1862	Cut through two miles east of Pamban i.e. through Rameshwaram Island (Alignment No. 2)
4.	Sir William Denson's	1863	Cut through four miles east of Pamban i.e. through Rameshwaram Island
5.	Mr. Stoddart's	1871	Cut through three miles east of Pamban i.e. through Rameshwaram Island
6.	Mr. Robertson's (Harbour Engineers of India)	1872	Cut through one mile east of Pamban i.e. through Rameshwaram Island.
7.	Sir John Code's (Consultant to South India Ship and Canal Port and Coaling Station Ltd. U.K)	1884	Same as Mr. Stoddart's i.e. through Rameshwaram Island
8.	South Indian Railway Engineers	1903	Along the coastline of Tamil Nadu i.e. from Shingle Islets and then through Rameshwaram Island.
9.	Sir Robert Briston's	1922	Same as South Indian Engineers i.e. through Rameshwaram Island

II. After Independence in 1947

10.	Ramaswami Mudaliar's	1956	Some miles west of Pamban (Alignment No. 1)
11.	Nagendra Singh	1967	Some sime southwest of Pamban i.e. through Rameshwaram Island. (Alignment No. 2)
12.	Lakshminarayana's	1983	About 1 km west of Kodandanaswami Temple i.e. through Rameshwaram Island (Alignment No. 3)
13.	S. Gopalan Steering Group's (Ministry of Surface Transport)-1	1997	Cut through East of Kodandaraman Temple i.e through Rameshwaram Island (Alignment 4)
14.	S. Gopalan Steering Group's-II	1998	Cut around Dhanushkodi (Alignment 5)
15.	NEERI's Initial–Initial Environmental Examination (IEE) Report	1998	Since Alignment 5 requires cutting through coral reefs by 'blasting during construction', hence *of all five alternate alignments*, Alignment 4 "has been identified as the best alternate which will cause least damage to biota and the environment."

16. Ministry of Environment & Forest, GOI	1999	After reviewing the IEE Report, the Ministry conveyed to the Ministry of Surface Transport in a letter dated April 8, 1999 that "Prima facie the Ministry is not in favour of this (SSCP) project". In October 1999, the DMK joined the NDA Government, and nominated four Ministers.
17. Minister of Surface Transport	2001	The Minister of Surface Transport on 9th March, 2001 approved drafting a fresh EIA and preparing a Detailed Feasibility Report to review the earlier (1999) rejection of the SSCP.
18. NEERI's	2002	In June 17, 2002, NEERI somersaulted and recommended a new Alignment No. 6 (See Annexure 1 to 3)
19. Cabinet Commission (CCEA) on Economic Affairs, GOI	2004	Approval given to SSCP, and Alignment No. 6 that cuts through the Rama Setu
20. Prime Minister	2005	Inauguration of the Project (see Box 2)

Moreover, the Government's insistence on sticking to the objectionable Alignment No. 6 Channel route despite all sustained arguments on grounds of economics, environment, national security, and above all the sanctity of the Rama Setu, holy to a billion Hindus, makes all patriotic citizens wonder whether there is a secret agenda behind this adamant attitude in wanting to destruct the Rama Setu when an alternative channel alignment was available. Moreover, the Government did not hestitate for a moment to alter routes in other projects e.g., reconstruction of certain proposed routes tunnels for the Delhi Metro. Islamic groups had earlier objected to the route proposed on the ground that vibrations from train movements could cause fracture of the Qutub Minar; or when in the Bangalore Metro project, that such vibrations could cause damage to Tipu Sultan's palace. Indeed the Metro tunnel direction was changed promptly on the orders of no less than the Prime Minister. *Then why, in the Rama Setu case, is there such resistance?* Given that the Tamil Nadu Chief Minister Mr. Karunanidhi is a self-proclaimed Rama-hating atheist, and that the United Progressive Alliance Chairperson Ms. Sonia Gandhi is a devout Catholic, and hence compliant to cues from the Vatican, would perhaps debasement of a Hindu icon be the secret agenda behind the wanton desire to destruct the Rama Setu? This possibility was hinted at by V. Sundaram, IAS (Retd), who while demitting his office as Chairman of the Tuticorin Port Trust and ex-officio member of the 1981 Lakshminarayan Committee wrote a letter to the Chairman of the Committee (See Annexure 20) stating *inter alia* that "I am rather concerned about the surreptious and subterranean efforts being made by the Catholic Church to influence the Government of India to somehow destroy the Ramar Sethu Bridge just in order to give a death blow to an ancient symbol of Hindu religion..." It is the author's submission that, by all objective counts, Hindus are under a siege today [see this author's *Hindus Under Siege*, Har-Anand, 2006] because of such secret agendas.

Rama Setu, as a world heritage should be protected and should not be destroyed in the name of a project which is of doubtful economic viability. To cut our nation's losses from this sick (and what now seems doomed) project, we can choose to create a land based channel like the Panama or Suez canals, through Mandappam. This would have locks on either side to prevent incursion of the turbulent waters of the Bay of Bengal into the serene waters of the Gulf of Mannar. It would also be shorter by about 39 nautical miles (an equivalent of about 6.5 hours saving in navigation time). In addition, if a plate tectonic inspired earthquake (resulting from the clash of the Indian and Eurasian/ Burmese plates) occurs, such a land-based channel close to the coastline of Bharatam, will facilitate rescue measures. It will also discourage terrorists like LTTE, smugglers, and narcotic traffic from using the channel. This is the alternative to damaging and desecrating the hoary Rama Setu. Even today, fisherfolk in Rameshwaram area try not to cause damage to Rama Setu; and if even a small piece of rock is chipped while collecting algae or corals, people perform *prayas'citam* (as penance or repentance) and seek divine compassion and forgiveness.

Therefore, "Om verses Rome" is the call that today signifies the rationale for the ongoing national movement to protect Rama Setu as our heritage. The Government of India under pressure from one of it's atheistic coalition components supported by foreign religions interests symbolised as 'Rome' wants this Rama Setu destructed in the name of dredging a furrow through the shallow Palk Straits to provide a channel deep enough to permit some ships to get passage from ports in the south to ports in the north.

'Om' is the primordial sound denoting supreme divinity in Bharatiya tradition. Rome signifies the Vatican which wants to harvest souls through devious strategies to promote evangelization and conversion of Bharatiyas into Christians, by a process of inducement and a denial of the heritage exemplified by Rama Setu (the man-made causeway built by Architect Nala). Om is the sound which emanates from a s'ankha (shank trumpet), called s'ankhanaada. This s'ankha, the shell turbinella pyrum, is a unique product available only along the coastline of Bharatam, in the Gulf of Mannar in particular where Rama Setu is located and where the Sethusamudram Channel Project, at a cost of over Rs. 2500 crores, is sought to be implemented as a channel passage cutting through this world heritage monument.

This project therefore should be stopped and re-evaluated, since a monument which ought to be protected by the state is sought to be desecrated. Defending Rama Setu is therefore our national duty.

Rama Setu together with the neighbourhood Marine Biosphere are world heritage sites, and it should have been deemed an ancient monument. There is overwhelming evidence to prove the existence of Rama Setu and its use as a land-bridge between Bharat and Sri Lanka for generations. On either side of the bridge there are sacred pilgrimage sites and temples, e.g., Shivalinga at Rameswaram and

Shivalinga at Tirukedeswaram (Mantota on the Sri Lanka side at the end of Talaimannar).

OBJECTIVE OF THE PROJECT

As stated above, by dredging the sea-bed in Palk Bay and Palk Strait, the Sethusamudram Ship Channel Project (SSCP) has the objective of creating a navigation channel from the Indian Ocean to the Bay of Bengal through the Gulf of Mannar, the Rama Setu, Palk Bay and the Palk Straits — a navigation channel of respectively 10m, 12m and 14m depth and 300-500 m width. The channel will utilize available natural depth for navigation in the Gulf of Mannar and some stretches of Palk Bay.

BENEFITS OF THE PROJECT

It is claimed by Government, that such a Project will lead to substantial savings in voyage time, in distance traversed, and fuel consumption, thereby benefiting the shipping industry and EXIM trade. Due to absence of navigable depths, even Coast Guard and Naval ships have to develop a Transhipment Hub in the Southern Peninsula, mainly due to the lack of a navigation channel linking Palk Bay and the Gulf of Mannar. However, the Admiral of the Indian Navy, and Chief of Naval staff Sureesh Mehta told journalists in Chennai on January 22, 2008 [*New Indian Express*] that the project "will be useful only for small ships and not for big ones navigative on international routes" thereby debunking the DMK's claim that the Navy can deploy its frigates, battleships and aircraft carriers through the Setu Channel. This has been further confirmed by the President of Institute of Marine Engineers (India) that only ships below 40,000 or less DWT can pass through the proposed channel. Moreover, for national security reasons, the Navy has never asked for a ship channel through the Palk Straits, since they are already using the Pambat sea pass route for small Coast Guard Boats. On January 31, 2008, at the anniversary function of the Coast Guard, the Director General, Vice Admiral Homi Contractor declared the SSCP as "a security threat" because it will facilitate the LTTE pirates dealers and narcotics.

Hence, considerable expenditure on anti-terrorist & pirate, and drug traffic monitoring would be required for the Navy, expenditure that has not been budgeted in the SSCP costs calculations. Then what are the benefits? The following major benefits are envisaged:

- SSCP will provide a shorter navigation route between on the one hand, Kanyakumari and Tuticorin, and on the other hand, the east coast ports of Chennai, Ennore, Kakinada, Visakhapatnam, Paradip, Haldia and Kolkata besides ports in neighbouring countries such as Chittagong.
- SSCP will facilitate coastal movement of domestic cargo leading to greater employment generation in the Ports and the industries situated in their hinterlands.
- Maritime trade in Tamilnadu – both coastal and international – will flourish with rapid development of the existing minor ports of Pondicherry, Cuddalore and Nagapattinam and the development of a new minor port in Ramanathapuram.
- Fishermen will be directly benefited because there is potential for developing fishing harbours (between Nagapattinam and Tuticorin) with proper landing and storage facilities.
- Development of existing major and minor ports and new ports will accelerate industrial development resulting in greater employment opportunities in manufacturing and service units.
- The channel will become an invaluable asset from the point of view of national defence and security as it will enable easier and quicker access between the coasts.
- Transhipment of India Cargo on foreign shores will gradually decrease, and after sometime stop altogether.

The question is how valid are these claims of the Government, and are these claims backed by scientific and economic analysts? *In this book, I propose to show that these claims are all bogus and bereft of any foundation in facts.*

CHAPTER 2

Sethusamudram Ship Channel Proposed Projects Since 1860

I. PRE-INDEPENDENCE PROPOSALS

Between 1860 and 1922, nine proposals were made for a Ship Channel across to connect the Gulf of Mannar and the Palk Bay for ocean-going ships plying between the West Coast of India and the East Coast (Table 1). In brief these were:

1. 1860 Commander Taylor's Proposal
2. 1861 Mr. Townshend's Proposal
3. 1862 Parliamentary Committee's Proposal
4. 1863 His Excellency Governor of Madras Sir William Dennison's Proposal
5. 1871 Mr. Stoddart's Proposal
6. 1872 Mr. Robertson's (Harbour Engineer for India) Proposal
7. 1884 Sir John Code's Proposal for South India Ship Canal, Port & Coaling Station, Limited
8. 1903 S.I Railway Engineer's Proposal based on their Survey
9. 1922 Sir Robert Bristow's (Harbour Engineer to the Government of Madras) Proposal

A brief survey of these various proposals extracted from various Reports is given hereunder.

1. *Commander Taylor's Proposal – 1860*

The earliest proposal was made in 1860 by Commander Taylor of the Indian Marine. He advocated cutting a canal (a channel cut only through land)) across the Tonitorai Peninsula at a place about 12 miles west of Pamban. At first stated its cost was estimated at only about £ 90,000; but further inquiries brought the estimate up to £1,500,000. Owing to the great expense involved and the extra work to be done in comparison with a canal across the Island of Rameswaram (see proposals 3to 9), the Scheme was not seriously considered.

2. *Mr. Townshend's Proposal – 1861*

Mr. Townshend proposed siting the canal through the Pamban Pass. His proposal was to deepen the existing tortuous Pamban Channel to enable the passage of large vessels. However, the objections to its adoption, with a curved channel, and subject to the strong currents through the Pamban Pass were so obvious that it put the scheme outside the pale of practical consideration.

3. *Parliamentary Committee's Proposal – 1862*

In 1862, a Committee of the British Parliament was appointed to report on the site for a canal across the Island of Rameswaram, and they recommended an alignment situated about two miles East of Pamban, crossing the Rameswaram, Island in a straight Northerly direction.

4. *Proposal of Sir William Dennison, Acting Governor of Madras – 1863*

In 1863, Sir William Dennison, then Acting Governor of Madras, visited Pamban and selected a site which he considered the most advantageous. This was about a mile future east from that recommended by the Parliamentary Committee. This alignment was unsuitable, as its southern entrance would be very much exposed during the South-West Monsoon.

5. *Mr. Stoddart's Proposal – 1871*

In 1871, Mr. Stoddart recommended a site about one mile west of Sir William Dennison's alignment and parallel to it. This was practically the same as the one suggested by the

Parliamentary Committee. This alignment was protected from the fury of the South West Monsoon by the reefs and small islands on the southern side ;its northern approach was, however, exposed to the North-East Monsoon. This alignment too was given up.

6. *Proposal of Mr. Robertson, Harbour Engineer to the Colonial Govt. of India – 1872*

In March, 1872, Sir Elphinstone, M.P., wrote to the Under Secretary of State for India, requesting that "Mr. Robertson, Harbour Engineer for India, should be directed to proceed to Pamban and examine the locality closely and minutely and give his opinion as to the best mode of proceeding in the matter, which is every month becoming of greater importance to the commerce and trade of the East".

Accordingly Mr. Robertson visited Pamban and selected a new site about a mile from Pamban with its southern entrance well within the protection of Kurisadi and Shingle Islands. Evidently, he did not make a close examination of the channel leading to the southern entrance, which would be narrow and would require an enormous amount of dredging to fit it for the passage of vessels.

7. *Sir John Code's Proposal – 1884*

In 1884, after a lapse of 12 years, "The South India Ship Canal Port and Coaling Station, Limited," U.K., considered the project for the construction of a canal across the Rameswaram Island and instructed Sir John Code, Consulting Engineer, to prepare a report and estimate. His report discussed the previous schemes and decided on the alignment for the canal. The Madras Government in their proceeding, dated the 14th October, 1890, however, advised the Government of India to reject the scheme on the ground that the shoals at the Palk Straits between Pt. Calimere and Pt.Pedro would prevent the projected canal being made use of by vessels of a deep-sea draft.

8. *South Indian Railway Engineer's Proposal – 1903*

In 1902, the South Indian Railway Company carried out a fresh survey by their Engineers and decided upon an alignment in Rameswaram about which they stated as follows:

"The final alignment of the canal has been determined after a careful survey was made of the seas on each side, and due consideration was given to its protection at both ends during the monsoons. A glance at the maps which accompany the project report will show that the minimum amount of dredging at the approaches will be required to enable a depth of 30ft. to be dredged. The southern entrance is well under the protection of the Kallaru reef with the Shingle Islets and also of the Kurisadi, Pulli-Vausel and Pulli Islands and their surrounding reefs which form a natural breakwater during the South-West Monsoon season.

The line of canal is oblique (and in the direction of the prevailing winds) and has the same advantage as advocated by Sir John Code in his alignment, which has already been referred to." But the proposal lay in cold storage.

9. *Proposal of Sir Robert Bristow Harbour Engineer to the Government of Madras – 1922*

After another two decades, Sir Robert Bristow, Harbour Engineer to the Government of Madras, made a thorough study of all the previous proposals and carried out detailed investigations and put up his proposal for an alignment somewhat similar to the previous one adopted by the South Indian Railway across the Rameswaram Island, as being the best line for the canal crossing.

II. POST-INDEPENDENCE PROPOSALS

The proposals considered after independence were as under:-

1. *Sethusamudram Project Committee – 1956*

   The committee was headed by Sir A. Ramaswamy Mudaliar and the committee contemplated a 26 foot draft land canal crossing the main land at Mandapam estimated to cost Rs. 1.8 crores. Capt. H.R. Davis carried out further survey in the year 1959 and suggested certain modifications, regarding alternative alignment across the main land maintaining the same draft. In 1961, Alignment No. 1 was suggested.

   In 1963, the Government of Madras under the guidance of its State Port Officer also explored the possibility of increasing the draft from 26 feet to 36 feet at an estimated cost of Rs. 21 crores.

2. *Nagendra Singh Committee Report – 1968*

   In 1964, the Government of India constituted a committee under the Chairmanship of Dr. Nagendra Singh, Secretary Ministry of Shipping and Transport. In 1968, the committee completed its report which contemplated a draft of 30 feet at an estimated cost of Rs. 37.46 crores. The committee examined the alignments suggested earlier; and because it was found that layers of sand stone were present in the Mandapam alignment, it suggested an alternative alignment in the Rameswaram Island crossing called the DE alignment near Thankachimadam. This was Alignment No. 2.

3. *The Lakshminarayan Committee Report – 1983*

   A committee under the Chairmanship of Shri H.R. Lakshminarayan, Development Advisor (Ports) was constituted in the year 1981. The committee collected the opinions and representations of leading members of the public, industrialists and Government officials of the State. Certain prominent citizens of the Rameswaram island represented that the channel would serve better if located to the east of Rameswaram town as far as possible, as it would otherwise affect the movement of pilgrims in the temple town. In 1983, after further detailed investigations a new alignment was proposed across Dhanushkodi, one km. west of Kodandaramasamy Temple across the narrow land strip known as the 'K' alignment. The committee also appointed a Navigational Expert Group to finalize the bottom width of the channel and the under keel clearance. The committee recommended construction of two channels called the south and north channels and also construction of a lock in the land portion connecting both the channels. This was Alignment No. 3.

4. *The Pallavan Transport Consultancy Services Report – 1996*

   In 1994, the State Government of Tamil Nadu felt that the Sri Lakshminarayan Committee Report of 1983 must be up dated and so it directed M/s. Pallavan Transport Consultancy Services Ltd. (PTCS). Tamil Nadu Government undertaking, to reappraise and revalidate the 1983 report. Fresh particulars of cost and traffic were collected and incorporated in this Report.

5. *Tuticorin Port Trust as Nodal Agency – 1997*

   In February, 1997, the Ministry of Surface Transport made Tuticorin Port Trust as the Nodal Agency for the Project; and subsequently in July 1997 the National Environmental Engineering Research Institute (NEERI), Nagpur was appointed by the Ministry of Surface Transport to prepare the Initial Environmental Examination (IEE) of the Project. On 29.10.1998, the IEE Study Report was submitted to a steering committee headed by Dr. S. Gopalan. It opined that after review of all the previously suggested five alternative routes, the NEERI was of the considered opinion that one particular alignment, Alignment No. 4 (which cut across the Pamban Island, east of Kothandaramasamy temple), would cause the least damage to the biota and the environment, and that with this alignment, the Project was environmentally safe and would have negligible effect on the eco system and the Marine National Park of the Gulf Mannar.

However a year later in 1998, NEERI suggested Alignment No. 5; but later still on realising that coral rocks would have to be blasted with explosives, it dropped that proposal too. Thereafter NEERI made a fresh presentation to the Minister of Environment and Forest on March 1999 on the IEE recommendations. Based on this presentation, the Ministry then sent a letter dated April 8, 1999 to the Ministry of Surface Transport stating that *prima facie* they were opposed to the entire project as it had serious environmental implications with respect to the Marine Park and the Biosphere Reserve located in the Palk Strait area. Hence, it was recommended to drop the Project altogether. In October 1999, the DMK jointed the NDA Government and the party's nominees became Ministers. The DMK was determined to push through the Project and enlisted Defence Minister Mr. George Fernandes to pursue the project with the Union Government. As a first step, NEERI was then asked by the Minister of Environment (a nominee of the DMK), to file the Final Report (FEE) of the Project. In December 2000, this FEE was submitted to the Ministry of Environment. Therein NEERI made a somersault: for the first time it suggested Alignment No. 6 route, which route called for cutting through the Rama Setu. This route had been considered by earlier committees beginning with the Mudaliar Committee of 1956 and it had been rejected by all of them.

On March 9, 2001, the Minister for Surface Transport Mr Arun Jaitely ordered a fresh study of the NEERI's FEE of the Project, including the suggestion of a new route cutting through Rama Setu, since the earlier five suggested routes had been rejected by the Ministry of Environment & Forests vide letter dated April 8, 1999 (Annexure 5). The Ministry also obtained approval of the PIB to prepare a Detailed Project Report and an Environmental Impact Assessment (EIA).

In February 2002, on the instructions of the Ministry of Environment, NEERI was entrusted with conducting the following two studies in regard to this alignment:

(*i*) A techno-economic viability study; and

(*ii*) An environmental impact assessment.

Thereafter in 2004, the Tuticorin Port Trust as the Nodal Agency engaged M/s.L & T – Ramboll Consulting Engineers, Chennai, to prepare a Detailed Project Report, which Report sought to establish the financial viability of the Project and also meet prescribed environmental standards "for preserving and conserving the rich bio-diversity in the project region". It adopted Alignment No. 6 (i.e., cutting through Rama Setu by breaching and dredging through the Setu). However, the Union Government failed to obtain from the Tamil Nadu Pollution Control Board the NOC that is mandatorily required, under Regulations framed by the Union Government itself. On July 2, 2005, the Prime Minister Dr Manmohan Singh, disregarding this illegality, meekly formally inaugurated the Project in Madurai. However the then Tamil Nadu Chief Minister, Ms. Jayalalitha boycotted the ceremony in protest against the failure of the Union Government to obtain the environmental impact analysis clearance from the State Government.

The UPA Government defends itself today by claiming that it was the NDA that had conceived the project including the dredging through the Rama Setu [Annexure 15]. The DMK President Mr Karunanidhi has published a booklet detailing the paper trail to prove that it was the BJP led NDA government which cleared the Alignment No. 6 calling for the destruction and defiling of the Rama Setu.

The truth, or otherwise of this implict but serious charge is however an irrelevant issue for this study. We oppose the SSCP calling for Rama Setu destruction, regardless of whoever had cleared it. The onus is, nevertheless, on the UPA to substantiate the charge by publishing a *White Paper* on the project, and for the BJP to defend its position, whatever it is, against the UPA charges.

CHAPTER 3

The Historicity and Heritage of Rama Setu

INTRODUCTION

According to Valmiki's *Ramayana,* Sri Rama told Lakshmana in Lanka: "*Jananee janmabhoomishca svargaadapi gariyasi*". As translated by Maharishi Aurobindo, this reads: "Mother and Motherland is greater by far than even heaven". These immortal words find an expression in Rama Setu or Sethubandha, a causeway bridge which is a symbol of the motherland. These immortal patriotic words attributed to Sri Rama, will remain in the Nation's memory as long as Hindustan lives as a continuing civilization; and hence, the Setu will always be revered. It is a heritage, a tirthasthaana, and a divyakshetram.

Speaking of the *Ramayana,* Jules Michelet (1798-1874), a famous French historian stated:

"The year 1863 will remain cherished and blessed. It was the first time I could read India's great sacred poem, the divine *Ramayana*..... This great stream of poetry carries away the bitter leaven left behind by time and purifies us. Whoever has his heart dried up, let him drench it in the *Ramayana*.... I have found what I was looking for: the bible of kindness. Great poem, receive me!... Let me plunge into it! It is the sea of milk."(See Michelet J: *La Bible de l'humanite,* volume 5 of OEuvres (Paris: Bibliotheque Larousse, 1930), p. 109-110).

It is in the background of this deep spiritual ambience pervading the Rama Setu, that retired Supreme Court Justice K.T. Thomas firmly stated : "Ram Sethu should not be broken": on April 5 2007, at an investiture ceremony at Rashtrapati Bhavan, New Delhi, where Justice Thomas had just received the Padma Bhushan from the President of India and in answer to a question from the media, he so replied:

"In projects like this (Sethusamudram Shipping Canal Project), decisions are to be based *not only on a study of geological implications*; the religious sentiments of the people are also to be taken into account. The religious sentiments of the people of Bharat have to be honoured by every government of India. There is a tradition in this land, of honouring religious sentiments. *So, it is my definite opinion that Ram Sethu must not be broken*". (emphasis supplied)

If only because of the sheer faith of the masses of India in Sri Rama, the Rama Setu must be declared an 'Ancient Monument' within the meaning of section 2 (a) of the Ancient Monuments and Archaeological Sites Act 1958 ; and it must be protected and nurtured as a revered national heritage.

Incidentally a monument does not have to be man-made to be declared an ancient monument. For example, the Brahmasarovar in Kurukshetra and the Shivalinga of Amarnath are natural phenomena. But both are believed to be of divine origin and so they have been notified as "ancient monuments". On February 6, 2008 the Prime Minister Dr. Manmohan Singh directed the Ministry of Culture to file with the UNESCO an appliction seeking 'World Heritage Site status for the Majuli Island, a deltaic island in the middle of the Brahmaputra River in the Jorhat District area of Assam. Similiarly, based on archaeological studies, textual evidences 'and Hindu traditions as well as the traditions of Muslims and Christians (who refer to the monument as Adam's Bridge), Rama Setu must be considered an ancient monument. Whether it is Rama Setu or

Adam's Bridge, both Rama and Adam are revered as ancients; and hence the Setu, associated with both of them, is an ancient monument.

In its judgement in *S. Veerabadran Chettiar v. E.V.Ramaswami Naicker* (AIR 1958 Supreme Court 1032 page 1035), the Supreme Court has observed as follows:

> "... Any object however trivial or destitute of real value in itself if regarded as sacred by any class of persons would come within the meaning of the penal section (295 of Indian Penal Code). Nor is it absolutely necessary that the object, in order to be held sacred, should have been actually worshipped. An object may be held sacred by a class of persons without being worshipped by them. It is clear, therefore, that the courts below were rather cynical in so lightly brushing aside the religious susceptibilities of that class of persons to which the complainant claims to belong. The section has been intended to respect the religious susceptibilities of persons of different religious persuasions or creeds. *Courts have got to be very circumspect in such matters, and to pay due regard to the feelings and religious emotions of different classes of persons with different beliefs, irrespective of the consideration whether or not they share those beliefs, or whether they are rational or otherwise, in the opinion of the court.*" (emphasis supplied).

After the above enunciation of the law, there is no room left not to respect the sentiments of the vast majority of Indians who regard the Rama Setu as an inalienable heritage. The word 'setu bandha' immediately evokes the sacred memory of Sri Rama, under whose direction the bridge was built. This tradition is not just an Indian tradition; but it is a pan-Asian tradition, a sacred memory in particular in the states on the rim of the Indian Ocean, populated by over 2 billion people.

To dismiss such sanctity as "imaginary" is also premature, since later developments in science can perhaps establish the reality of the Rama Setu. For example, earlier both the Sarasvati river and Dwarka city were considered by certain historians to be imaginary. Now modern science, based on archaeology, has established their existence. And if it were destroyed/damaged and later it was discovered that in fact the Rama Setu was partially or wholly the work of ancient human hands, what an incalculable loss it would be for all mankind!

Finally, other objects of sanctity could also be castigated as "imaginary" on the basis that there is no scientific proof for them. What, for instance, if it is said that the claim of the sacred hair in the Hazratbal Mosque in Srinagar is imaginary— since there is no proof that it actually belonged to the Islamic Prophet Mohammed? ....Or that the birth of Jesus is imaginary? ....yet, saying so is so offensive that it is inconceivable that the Government would file an affidavit so stating (as it did in the case of Sri Rama and the Rama Setu)..

It is our responsibility, our dharma, to protect, preserve and cherish a monument associated with Sri Rama We must preserve the Rama Setu from desecration, no matter the cost.

THE SIGNIFICANCE OF SRI RAMA TO BOTH HINDUS AND NON-HINDUS

Why is Sri Rama such a magnet for the Hindu masses, irrespective of caste? The question may puzzle some people who do not know India, because Sri Rama neither performed any miracle on his own, nor did he himself ever claim to be an *avatara* of Lord *Maha Vishnu*. Nevertheless, after so many millennia, the *Ramayana* is still evergreen; and Rama Lila is celebrated with gusto and rejoicing every year in every part of our nation. Sri Rama and his associates immortalized in *Ramayana,* have endeared themselves to millions of people all over the world, transcending even religious barriers as the earlier quote from Iqbal shows.

The awareness of the greatness of Sri Rama is not limited only to humans on earth. There is a very enlightening dialogue between Lord Shiva and his spouse Parvati which occurs in the concluding part of *Vishnu Sahasranamam* in the epic, *Mahabharata.Vishnu Sahasranamam* is a recital of the one thousand names of Lord

Mahavishnu. Therein occurs a conversation between Bhishma and Yudhistra. Yudhistra had addressed the following questions to Bhishma: "Who is the one God? What is the supreme goal? What is the highest duty of man? How can man reach the highest end of life?" To this Bhishma replied that the Supreme Being is omnipresent and therefore rightly called *Maha Vishnu,* and that His thousand names ward off all sin and fear. Then, in one hundred and seven stanzas, Bhishma recited the one thousand names of *Maha Vishnu* in succession. Towards the very end Goddess Parvathi enquired of Lord Shiva, in the following *sloka,*

"*Kenopayena Laguna Vishnor Nama Sahasraham*
Patyathe Pandithair Nithyam Srothumichamyaham Prabhoh:"

(*i.e* "Does there exist any abridged version of this garland of one thousand names, which will have the same efficacy as reciting all the thousand names?").

To this, Lord Shiva replied to Parvathi as follows:

"*Rama Rama Ramethi, Rame Rame Mano Rame*
Sahasra Nama Thattulyum Rama Nama Varanane:"

(*i.e.* "the recital of just the one word 'Rama' will produce an effect equivalent to reciting all the thousand names of *Maha Vishnu:*")

Therefore, even gods and goddesses themselves felt the power and the charm of Sri Rama: hence why would it surprise anyone if ordinary mortals worship this Lord?

The worship of Sri Rama pervades not only India but many other countries in South-East Asia. For instance, in Thailand, there is a province called *Ayutthya* (Ayodhya), wherein about 75 kilometres north of Bangkok, there is a Rama temple. According to historians, this *Ayutthya* bears testimony to Ram Rajya. Longstanding cultural contacts existed with the Kingdom of Thailand upto 1344 AD; and at that time King U-thong (*Uttanga* in Sanskrit) who ruled at a place called Nong Sano, named his capital *Ayutthya* after the capital city in India from which the Raghuvansi King Rama ruled. U-thong adopted his name as Ramathibodi, which in Sanskrit, means "the king under the empire of Rama". It is also said that Rama's son, Lava, visited *Ayutthya*. There are more than 400 temples of Rama and Sita in Thailand alone.

Sikhs believe that their first two Gurus, Guru Nanak and Guru Angad Dev (both belonging to the Vedi clan) were descendants, in the seventeenth generation, of Lava, the elder of the twin sons of Sri Rama; while the other eight Gurus, namely, Guru Amardas, Guru Ramdas, Guru Arjun, Guru Hargobind, Guru Hari Rai, Guru Harikrishnah, Guru Teghbahadur, and Guru Gobind Singh (all belonging to the Sodi clan) were descendants of Kusha, the other son of Sri Rama.. Sikhs believe that just as Allah is the ultimate God for Muslims, so in their holy book, *Guru Grant Sahib*, Sri Rama is referred to as the Almighty One God. The name Rama occurs in more than 100 places in the holy book. Some of the references are extracted below:

VILAVAL MAHALLA FIFTH. (Chand)
Aang Sri Guru Granth Sahib Ji 846
MALLAR MAHALLA FOURTH
Aang Sri Guru Granth Sahib Ji 1265-1266
SORATH MAHALLA NINTH
Aang Sri Guru Granth Sahib Ji 631

According to some Sikh scholars, just as Lord Rama is the *avatar* of Lord Maha Vishnu in the Treta Yug and Lord Krishna in the Dwapra Yug, Guru Gobind Singh is the avatar of Lord Maha Vishnu in the Kali Yug.

CRITICISMS OF THE HISTORICITY OF SRI RAMA AND THE RAMAYANA

Yet after all these citations, the English-enslaved mindset of certain contemporary intellectuals of India refuses to accept the historicity of Sri Rama: to such persons the Ramayana and the Mahabharatha are merely 'mythology'.

In 1813, James Mill and Charles Grant from the East India Company's Haileybury College, wrote the book "History of India" wherein they classified most of the literature of India as 'mythological'. Thereafter the Indian tutees in an Anglo-Indian educational system operated in English medium, just repeated this appellation like trained parrots. Mill and Grant classified these texts as mythological on the following premises:

1. The events described in these texts seem to have occurred before the date of creation of the earth (fixed by Father James Usher at 9 AM on 23rd Oct, 4004 BCE). Hence, it was argued, these texts which describe India and the existence of its civilization prior to this time could not be real and must be mythical or imaginary.

But of course Father Usher has now been proven wrong by modern cosmology and traditional archeological finds. Hence this premise of Mill and Grant is without basis.

2. Basing themselves on selfserving Greek texts, the eighteenth and nineteenth century British historians held that Alexander defeated Porus in 326 BCE and that it was he who had spread Greek culture and thereby civilized India and that until then Indians were uncivilized barbarians. But the civilization described in the Ramayana and Mahabharatha texts (both predating Alexander) seemed to be advanced in science, technology, culture, philosophy and linguistics. Hence, it was argued, they could not have existed prior to the arrival of Alexander and hence the texts must be mythical.

But thereafter, not only has the existence of a civilized India prior to the arrival of Alexander, been proved beyond doubt, but also the talk of the defeat of Porus at the hands of Alexander is now being questioned : after all it is certain that Alexander turned back after reaching the Indus—which he was unlikely to have done had he been victorious. Certainly too, no reference to Alexander survives in contemporary Indian texts, so it does not appear that Alexander created any sort of impression—let alone a deep cultural impression—on the India of his days. Hence this premise of Mill and Grant is also baseless.

3. The British came up with the concept of the 'Aryan Invasion of India' (which is stated to have occurred around 1500 BC), which

spread its culture and civilized Indians who until then were uncivilized barbarians. Hence, again, it was argued that the civilization described in these texts, which seemed to be more advanced in science, technology, culture, philosophy and linguistics could not have existed prior to the Aryan Invasion and hence the texts must be mythical.

But today, the idea of an Aryan Invasion has been dismissed even by Western historians as a figment of imagination and a concoction by the British imperialists to justify their occupation of India: their argument being that they (i.e. the British), are as legitimate occupiers of Indian territory and as legitimate beneficiaries of India's natural resources as foreigners of the Aryan race, who had invaded and settled in India and supplanted the original inhabitants of the Dravidian race. This Aryan – Dravidian classification has now been proven to be racially incorrect: modern DNA analysis has determined that despite their differences in features and complexion (which differences are now traced to local factors, temperatures and pigmentation), most Indians belongs to the same race. Also the study of traditional Indian texts has brought to light how the terminology 'Dravidian' was based on geographical division and was not racial, cultural or civilizational. The various Indian languages have a common Sanskrit vocabulary of upwards of 40 percent and they also have a similar syntax; and all their scripts have evolved from Brahmi. Thus this premise of Mill and Grant is likewise fatally flawed.

4. Mill and Grant also held that the texts were mutually inconsistent and hence the texts must be imaginary or mythical. It is to be noted that while the texts are alleged to be inconsistent, nevertheless British historians and their Indian tutees have uncritically accepted the genealogy in the Puranas (otherwise, for example, how do historians of all schools, Western and Indian, know that Ashoka was the son of Bindusara or that Samudragupta was the son of Chandra Gupta, or that the Maurya dynasty succeeded the Nandas

except from the same 'mythical' *Puranas*?). Given this, gaps or inconsistencies in narration cannot detract from the historicity of the texts. Logically therefore we cannot accept a part of a source but not the whole, after reconciling the apparent inconsistencies in the source material.

Thus, it is submitted, all the premises of Mill and Grant for classifying Indian literature as mythological are flawed.

Much to the consternation of—or perhaps jealousy as well of— British trained historians, there is no other civilization as ancient and continuous as India's.

THE ESTABLISHED TEXTUAL EVIDENCE OF RAMA

Valmiki, the author of the original Ramayana text was a contemporary of Sri Rama. This has been explicitly stated in the text itself. This story was not penned a few hundred years after Sri Rama. In fact, Valmiki was the guardian of the wife and sons of Sri Rama. Thus the Valmiki Ramayana has all the credibility attached to a contemporary historical account. If we look at various historical texts the world over, we find that authors have generally written about stories which happened a few hundred or even a few thousand years prior to their times. In such historical texts, the authenticity and the exactness of the material can be questioned.

Ramayana being a popular story of India, many authors down the centuries have written their own versions of Ramayana. Kalidasa, the great Sanskrit poet of the 5th century CE wrote his *Raghuvamsa*, his poem on Sri Rama and his forebears. The Tamil poet Kamban wrote his version of Kamba Ramayana over 1000 years back. Goswami Tulsidas wrote *Ram Charita Manas* in the 17th century. These three and many other eminent authors across India have penned the story eulogising Sri Rama and emphasizing his divinity.

The Puranas of India also mention the details of the story of Sri Rama. The stories mentioned in the Puranic texts and the original Ramayana of Valmiki cross validate each other in many places. This adds further credibility to the Valmiki Ramayana text being rightly termed as *Itihaasa* (*i.e.,* "it thus happened"), a historical text.

VALIDATION BY PLACE NAMES

Dr. Ram Avatar spent 25 years in researching whether the locations described in the Ramayana can be located in modern India. In particular, he was able to locate and photograph many of the spots through which Sri Rama traveled on his journey from Ayodhya to Sri Lanka (see Figure 3) and he has documented these with photographs in his monograph *Jahan Jahan Ram Charan Chali Jayi* ("Wherever the Footsteps of Rama fell"), published in 2007.

SKY CHARTING OR ARCHEO-ASTRONOMY

Planetarium software is a tool that, given a date in future or past and vice-versa, helps to arrive at planetary positions i.e. given a set of planetary configurations, one can arrive at the dates on which such configurations occurred, either in the future or in the past. There are probably over 50 different software available for this purpose. Each software can be used specifically for a particular application, like plotting the current night sky chart, predicting eclipses and the like. The person who has pioneered research on the topic is Shri D.K. Hari of Bharath Gyan.

When a spacecraft is launched for a journey to far-off planets like Jupiter or Saturn, its travel time would be well over 12 years. The software helps determine orbital positions of the planets when the spacecraft reaches their orbits. Naturally then, a high level of precision is required in the software.

Unlike that of any other civilization so far, it is a characteristic of the literature of the Indian civilization that there are innumerable accounts where some event is recounted along with night sky observations of the time of that event. By feeding the observations of the planetary configurations into the planetarium software, we can obtain the English calendar dates when these configurations could have occurred in the past. When these dates are logically arranged along with the events, it helps us to scientifically assign dates to events mentioned in Indian legends and historical texts, and thus it goes a long way towards validating them. This would be particularly true where there are no inconsistencies in such correlation of event and night sky configuration. In fact, it would be a stupendous and scientifically acceptable method of dating such event. A whole new and valid methodology of dating ancient events emerges, with exciting possibilities.

Thus the astronomical data left behind in our literature can be analysed scientifically to arrive at historic dates for various events. This approach is parallel to archaeology where physical remains are analysed to arrive at historic dates : it gives rise to a new branch of scientific dating which may be called Archaeo-astronomy. Many Indian researchers have made use of this software to arrive at historic dates for various events described in the literature. They have collated the outputs of such work that are worthy of scrutiny. (It should be made clear that the planetary combinations occur cyclically in time. Hence the same planetary combination could be seen not just in the present Yug but also for example in the Treta Yuga i.e., 17,50,000 years ago. This is the only weakness in this calculation; and it has been unscrupulously used by Western researchers to sneer at ancient Indian history: on the argument that human events could not have credibly occurred 17,50,000 years ago).

The works of Pushkar Bhatnagar, on the Historicity of Sri Rama form the basis of what is presented here to know the possible dates of the events in Sri Rama's lifetime.

Table 2 Historical Dates of Sri Rama

Events of Sri Rama	Date
Sri Ram Navami – Birthday	January 10, 5114 BCE (i.e. 7122 years ago)
Birth of Bharatha	January 11, 5114 BCE
Pre-coronation eve	January 4, 5089 BCE
Khar, Dushan episode	October 7, 5077 BCE

Vali Vadham	April 3, 5076 BCE
Hanuman's Visit to Lanka	September 12, 5076 BCE
Hanuman's Return from Lanka	September 14, 5076 BCE
Army march to Lanka	September 20, 5076 BCE

Source: Bhatnagar, Pushkar: *Dating the Era of Lord Ram*

The dates arrived at for the events in Table 2 above tally with the chronological sequence for the events as found in the Ramayana text: in fact the elapsed time between the events as indicated by these dates tallies with the elapse-time and their duration/age as described in the Ramayana. But (as pointed out in the last paragraph) the problem with this calculation is that planetary configuration is cyclic in time. This same configuration would occur once every 7122 years, and hence we need more evidence before we can rule out Tretayuga or confirm the above dates.

RAMA SETU DEPICTIONS IN VALMIKI'S RAMAYANA

In his Ramayana, Maharshi Valmiki has described the construction of the 'Setu' known to the nation for several millennia as 'Rama Setu'; and to the British, since the 19th century, as 'Adams Bridge'. The Ramayana states that this was built in a record time of 5 days under the leadership of Nala, the son of Viswakarma; that in Treta Yuga, following the advice of Samudraraja (who picked the site for Sri Rama, to thank Sri Rama for having saved him from Lord Shiva's ire), Sri Rama asked Nala to construct a dam on the sea to Srilanka; that Nala agreed, and under his direction, the Vanaras went in all directions and brought coral rocks, stones, trees, felled or uprooted, and built the 48 kilometre long and 3 kilometre wide causeway-like structure to enable Sri Rama's army to walk across to Sri Lanka.

The *vanara* sena uprooted rocks which are stated to resemble "huge elephants", using machines; and they brought them to the sea shore with the help of carrier vehicles. "The dam constructed by Nala who was as skilled and talented as his illustrious father,

resembled the milky way", says Valmiki. "The joyous roar raised by
the vanaras on completion of the dam silenced even the deadliest
noise of the mighty ocean". [Sarukkam 22, sloka 51-75]

In another verse, (this occurs in the 'Yuddha Kanda' of Adyatma
Ramayanam), Valmiki recites the words of Sri Rama returning with
Sita in a Pushpaka Vimana as follows: "Here is the Sethubandhana
worshipped by three worlds. It is a holy place. It has the ability to
relieve all the greatest of sins. It was here that Mahadeva [Lord Siva]
extended his whole hearted support to me earlier." [*Yuddha Kandam*
– 126.20.1].

About the actual construction of the Rama Setu, various stanzas
of the Valmiki Ramayana give minute, graphic and marvelously
evocative details. Thus:

> "At Rama's command, those lions among the monkeys entered
> the mighty forest with alacrity in hundreds and thousands on
> every side and those leaders of the simian tribes, tearing up the
> rocks, which in size they resembled, and the trees also dragged
> them to the sea and they covered the ocean with Sala, Ashvararna,
> (list of tree names).Those foremost monkeys transported those
> trees, with or without roots, bearing them like so many standards
> of Indra (the king of heaven) and they heaped (list of tree names)
> here and there. With the aid of mechanical devices, those
> powerful colossi dug up stones as big as elephants and rocks, and
> the water suddenly spouted into the air only to fall instantly.
> Thereafter those monkeys churned up the sea by rushing into it
> on all sides pulling on the chains."…

> "That immense causeway constructed by Nala in the bosom of
> the sea was built by the arms of those monkeys of formidable
> exploits and it extended over a hundred leagues."…

> "Some brought trunks of trees and others set them up; it was by
> hundreds and thousands that those monkeys, like unto giants,
> made use of reeds, logs and blossoming trees to construct that

bridge, rushing hither and thither with blocks of stone resembling mountains or the peaks of crags, which, flung into the sea, fell with a resounding crash."...

"The first day those monkeys resembling elephants, of immense energy, full of high spirits and exceedingly merry, erected fourteen leagues of masonry. The second day, those highly active monkeys of formidable stature set up twenty leagues. Bestirring themselves, those giants threw twenty-one leagues of structure over the ocean on the third day and on the fourth, working feverishly, they built up twenty-two leagues in extent. The fifth day, those monkeys, industrious workers, reached to twenty-three leagues distance from the further shore."...

"That fortunate and valiant son of Vishvakarma (architect of the demigods), leader of the monkeys, constructed a causeway worthy of his sire over the ocean and that bridge erected by Nala over the sea, the haunt of whales, dazzling in its perfection and splendor, was like the constellation of Svati in space."...

"Then the gods, Gandharvas, Siddhas (living beings superior to humans) and supreme Rishis (great sages) assembled in the sky, eager to see that masterpiece, and the gods and Gandharvas gazed on that causeway, so difficult of construction, that was ten leagues in width and a hundred in length built by Nala."...

"Those monkeys thereafter dived, swam and shouted at the sight of that unimaginable marvel that was almost inconceivable and caused one to tremble! And all beings beheld that causeway thrown over the ocean and by hundreds and thousands of kotis (millions), those monkeys, full of valor, having built that bridge over the immense repository of waters, reached the opposite shore."...

"Vast, well-constructed, magnificent with its wonderful paved floor, solidly cemented, that great causeway like unto a line traced on the waves, resembled the parting of a woman's hair."...

"Meanwhile Vibishana (brother of Ravana who joined Rama), mace (club) in hand, held himself ready at his post with his companions in case of an enemy attack. Thereafter Sugriva addressed Rama, who was valiant by nature, saying "Mount on the shoulders of Hanuman ;and Laxmana (brother of Rama) mount on those of Angada. O Hero, vast is this ocean, the abode of whales; those two monkeys who freely range the sky will transport you both.".…

"Then the fortunate Rama and Laxmana advanced thus and that magnanimous archer was accompanied by Sugriva. Some monkeys strode forward in the center, some threw themselves into the waves, some sprang into the sky, others marched on the bridge, some ranged through space like birds, and the terrific tumult of the trampling of that formidable army of monkeys drowned the roar of the ocean.".…

"When those simian troops had passed over the sea by the grace of Nala's causeway, the king ordered them to camp on the shore which abounded in roots, fruits and water.".…

"At the sight of that masterpiece that had materialized under the command of Raghava (another name of Lord Rama), despite the difficulties, the gods, who had drawn near with the Siddhas and Charanas as also the great Rishis, anointed Rama in secret there, with water from the sea, and said: "Mayest thou be victorious over thy foes, O Thou, who are a God among men! Do Thou rule over the earth and the sea eternally!".…

"Thus in various auspicious words, did they acclaim Rama in the midst of the homage offered to him by the Brahmins.".…

(From *The Ramayana* of Valmiki, Yuddha Kanda in Chapter 66: "The Great Causeway")

Thus, according to Valmiki, was constructed the great causeway Rama Setu. It survived as a causeway for several millennia; and it remained in use into recent historical times. Even as recently as 1478 A.D., it was known to be in use as a footbridge cum causeway to cross over from India to Srilanka. It is this Rama Setu, described above, that we see even today from Dhanushkodi across to Talaimanar in Sri Lanka [Satellite photo imaging by NASA & ISRO – see Figure 1]. It is this sacred Setu that the Government today wants demolished in the name of building a channel furrowed out of the shallow ocean floor in the Palk Straits.

In *Skanda Purana* (VI.101.1-44) describes the installation of three Shiva linga at the end, middle and beginning of Rama Setu is described. This is also related in *Kurma Purana* (21.10-61).

Garuda Purana (1.811.-22) listes sacred placed including Setubandh and Rameswar. Narada Purana (Uttara Bhag 76.1-20), extols the greatness of Rama-Setu.

Other appreciations of and references to Sri Rama, also occur as follows:

(a) Within India

The sheer divine beauty of Rama's personality inspired the poet Iqbal to declare him the 'Imam-E-Hind':

"Hai Ram key wujood pey Hindostan ko naaz
Ahl-e-nazar samajhte hain usko Imam-e-Hind
Ejaaz ous chiraagh-e-hidaayet kaa hai yahee
Raushantar azsaher haizamane main sham-e-Hind."

In short, Ram is the spiritual head of India, even according to Iqbal, who was a devout Muslim.

It was largely the work of Tamil saints such as Alwars and Nayanmars that the depiction of Sri Rama evolved from that of a young prince of Ayodhya to that of a divine avatar. Hence Sri Rama symbolizes India's unity of North and South, just as Krishna unifies East and West.

(b) In China

Interestingly, the Chinese Ambassador to India Sun Yuxi told me recently that there has been an ongoing scholarly debate in China, about the origins of the Monkey-hero Sun Wukong in the Chinese epic novel *Xiyouji* viz., does his origin stem from Hanuman, or is Sun Wukong a product of indigenous Chinese folklore?

The theory of a possible connection between Sun Wukong and Hanuman was first mooted by Hu Shih, the well known poet and President of Beijing University. In 1936, at the Harvard University Tercentennial Celebrations, Dr. Hu delivered a seminal speech entitled "Indianisation of China". Therein he spoke disapprovingly of the Chinese people swallowing and digesting Hinduism in the garb of Mahayana Buddhism, and accepting idol worship. In its way, in debunking Hindu culture, Dr. Hu's speech was as seminal as the nineteenth century Minute of Macaulay which resulted in a new trend of downplaying and attempting to obliterate all traces of India's native culture.

Like the Rama tradition in India, its tradition in the <u>Xiyouji</u> (translated as *Journey to the West*) has had a profound impact upon Chinese society. The Xiyouji is one of the most popular and well-known novels in the canons of Chinese literature.

The Xiyouji epic is based on the real life journey of Xuanzang (Hsieung Tsang in India literature) also known by the Buddhist honorific *Tripitaka*. Xuanzang traveled to India along the overland route of the Silk Road. In this epic novel, Tripitaka (i.e. Xuanzang) is accompanied by four disciples: Sun Wukong, Zhu Bajie, Sha Heshang, and the Dragon Prince (the last appears in the form of a white horse). The novel begins with the birth and early years of Sun Wukong, the hero of the novel. The first six chapters, recount Sun Wukong's quest for immortality, his unruly behavior, and finally his capture and punishment. From Chapter Six to the end of the novel, the plot focuses on the birth of Tripitaka and his pilgrimage to Buddha's mountain, where he obtains certain sutras.

Unlike Southeast Asian civilization, Chinese civilization after the Ching dynasty (1642 to1911) had begun to develop independently of India's cultural influence. This is not the case elsewhere in Asia; and thus the impact of Indian culture today is not as powerful in

China as it is in Southeast Asia. Nevertheless, several elements of Chinese culture, including literature, were affected by the culture of Hindustan. [For an authoritative account thereof, see Dr. Hera S.Walker's "Indigenous or Foreign: A Look at the Origins of the Monkey Hero Sun Wukong", Sino   Platonic Papers, 81 (September1998) [http://www.sinoplatonic.org/abstracts/spp081_monkey.html].

(c) Elsewhere in Asia

Likewise, the Rama tradition is not only pervasive in India, but is known and studied throughout Southeast Asia. Throughout the whole of Asia, representations of monkey figures are depicted in oral narration, theater, art, and, in modem times, television shows. Shrines have been erected by devout worshippers to pay homage to them. Clearly, the popularity of these monkey heroes is without question.

There are hundreds of renditions of the Rama saga within India alone. The Ramayana of Valmiki, who is claimed by Dalits of India as their own, is reputed to be the most prestigious and the most comprehensive of all the renditions. Hanuman is the monkey-general of the Monkey-king Sugriva. By the king's command, Hanuman is ordered to aid Prince Rama, the central hero of the saga, in finding his captive wife, Sita, abducted by the demonic titan Ravana. Hanuman occupies a central role in the search and rescue of Sita. He is the one who finds Sita and leads the charge against the titan army to rescue her.

So how was the Rama tradition transmitted to Southeast Asia and China? Trade, more than any other factor, provided different civilizations with a vehicle for cultural exchange, motivating people to cross over mountains, deserts, and large bodies of water. Of all the civilizations that participated in long-distance trade across the Eurasian landmass and throughout the eastern oceans, India's was one of the most influential. In an overview of history it is easy to see the effect left by India's culture in the arts, statecraft, and religion of many Southeast Asian countries. For example, the early plastic arts of Cambodia, Thailand, and Malaysia exhibit a strong Indian flavor in their style and subject matter.

(d) Sri Lankan references

Very recently, in order to attract Indian tourists in a big way, the Sri Lanka Tourism Development Authority (SLTDA) has formed a committee to work out an ambitious scheme to develop and promote as many as 34 sites in the island associated with the Ramayana, as set out below. [Box 2]

Ravana had brought Sita to Sri Lanka in a flying machine called "Pushpaka Vimanam" by the Hindus and "Dandu Monara Yanthraya" by the Sinhalese Buddhists. This landed at Werangatota, about 10 km from Mahiyangana, east of the hill station of Nuwara Eliya in central Sri Lanka. Sita was then taken to Goorulupota, now known as Sitakotuwa, where Ravana's wife Mandodari lived. Seetakotuwa is about 10 km from Mahiyangana on the road to Kandy. There Sita was housed in a cave at Sita Eliya, situated today on the highway that links Colombo with Nuwara Eliya. A temple dedicated to her exists there even today. Sita is believed to have had her bath in the mountain steam flowing beside this temple.

These are not the only sites in Sri Lanka associated with the Ramayana:

(a) North of Nuwara Eliya, in Matale district, is Yudhaganapitiya, where the Rama-Ravana battle is reputed to have taken place.

(b) Again, according to a Sinhalese legend, Dunuwila is the place from where Rama shot the "Bramshira" arrow (Brahmastra) that killed Ravana.

(c) Ravana made his battle plans in a place called Lakgala. This is a rock from the top of which Ravana could see northern Sri Lanka clearly. It served as a watchtower following the expectation that Sri Rama would invade the island to rescue his Sita. It was at Lakgala that Sri Rama's killer arrow is said to have struck Ravana.

Ramayana Sites in Srilanka

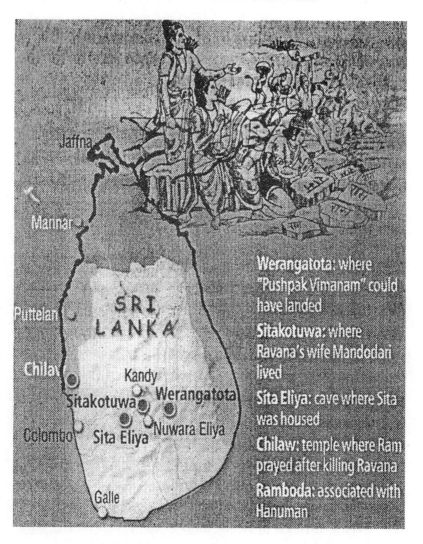

Jaffna

Mannar

Puttelan

Chilaw

SRI LANKA

Kandy

Sitakotuwa

Werangatota

Colombo

Sita Eliya

Nuwara Eliya

Galle

Werangatota: where "Pushpak Vimanam" could have landed

Sitakotuwa: where Ravana's wife Mandodari lived

Sita Eliya: cave where Sita was housed

Chilaw: temple where Ram prayed after killing Ravana

Ramboda: associated with Hanuman

(*d*) Thereafter, the scriptures say, Ravana's body was placed on the rock at Yahangala for his subjects to pay their last respects; and this place is pointed out even today.

(*e*) Since Ravana was a Brahmin, it was considered a sin to kill him, even in battle. To wash off the sin, Sri Rama prayed at the Munneswaram temple in Chilaw, 80 km north of Colombo.

(*f*) At Manaweri, north of Chilaw, is the temple Sri Rama is said to have gifted.

(*g*) Rumassala and Ramboda, also in the tea-growing central highlands, are associated with Hanuman. It is believed that Hanuman dropped the Dronagiri mountain, which he brought from the Himalayas, at Rumassala. At Ramboda, known for its massive waterfalls, a temple for Hanuman has sprung up. Legend has it that the Koneswaram temple, in the eastern district of Trincomalee, was a gift to Ravana from Shiva.

The documents available in Sri Lanka state that at the Buddha Vihara at Kelani, near Colombo, there is a representation of Rama handing over the "captured" Sri Lanka to Ravana's brother Vibheeshana, who sided with him in his conflict with Ravana.

SYNOPSIS AND CRITIQUE OF ALL THE ABOVE

It is therefore completely false to propagate, as DMK leader Mr. Karunanidhi has been doing, that Sri Rama is merely a North Indian God. There are historical evidences aplenty to show that the worship of Sri Rama as a divinity, took birth and evolved in the South, the 'Dravida' country, *and later got assimilated into the religious psyche of the North.* There are also inscriptional evidences to dismiss the attempt to link the rise of the worship of Sri Rama to the 'Islamic' invasion of North India in the 12th-13th centuries.

In her S.C. Misra Memorial Lecture entitled "The Making of a Hegemonic Tradition: The Cult of Rama Dasarathi", delivered at the 67th Session of the Indian History Congress, where she was later elected as President, Professor Suvira Jaiswal said that it was possible to "trace the gradual emergence of a full-fledged Rama cult in the Dravida country". The Vaishnavite saints of the south, the Alwars sang in praise of the local cult-spots as sanctified by the presence of their favourite deities. This gave scope for the identification of various places as scenes of events associated with the characters of Ramayana and celebration of the existing temples as those of Sri Rama.

Clear evidence of the setting up of shrines to Sri Rama as an incarnation of Vishnu, was available from the 10th century onwards in the Chola and Pandya kingdoms, which had been the locale of Alwar activities, Professor Jaiswal said.

Although the Chola kings were worshippers of Siva and constructed magnificent Siva temples, several of them assumed titles suggestive of their identification with Rama. For instance, Aditya Chola (AD 871-907), who claimed to have built several Siva temples on the banks of the Cauvery, assumed the title 'Kodandarama.' His son Paranthaka I called himself Samgraama Raghavam, i.e; Rama in battle.

In the Ananda Ramayanam, the commencement of the construction of the dam is described as follows: "Rama, who hails from Raghu Dynasty, installed the idol of Lord Vinayaka after giving directions about the dam to Nala. Then Rama worshipped the nine stones installed by Nala, representing the nine planets. This can be seen even today on the way from Ramanathapuram to Mandappam. He then conveyed his willingness to Hanuman about installing a wonderful linga in his name where the three seas meet. It is this area that Adi Sankara had described as 'Dravida' to Mandana Mishra in the epic *Sashtratha* (debate)in Varanasi."

"The mountain like dam 'Nalasethu' was built on the orders of Rama" says Vyasa in his Mahabharatha [3.267.45]

References to Rama in the Puranas

The *Bhagavatha Puranam* says that Balarama went to the dam "which can purify even the greatest sins". i.e. 'Samudhram Se Mahamath Mahapataka Nasanam', [10th Skandam-Sarukkam 79]

The *Padma Puranam* says, "this sethu was built by me within three days with the help of Vanara Sena." [Srusti kandam-Sarukkam 38]

The Skanda Purana says "the mere vision of Rama Sethu will relieve one from Samsara bandhas." [Sethu Mahatmiya Kandam-Sarukkam 1]

Thus, the Puranas say that the dam Sethu was built in the middle of the sea by Rama and ordain that it is a holy spot.

References to the Rama Setu in Tamil Literature

There is a reference to the Sethu in the Tamil Sangam classic, Akananuru, where a comparison is made between the uproar that occurred in a certain village clash, and "the sound heard from the sea near Thriuvanaikkarai (Adi Sethu), in Pandya Kingdom which was built by Rama, the great warrior".

In his Pasurappadi Ramayanam, Periyavaccan Pillai, one of the Vaishnava Acharyas, writes

"Malaiyal Anaikatti Marukarai eri". [from the elevated bund, he (Rama) crossed the coast (to Sri Lanka)]

'Sethu Puranam' also known as 'Sethu Mahatmiyam' is a Sangam era classic which contains 45 Sarukkas and 3438 verses, written by Niramba Alagiya Singar in the 16th Century. Recently it has been verified by Nallur Arumuga Navalar of Jaffna and published by Chidambaram Saivapprakasa Vidyasala Dharmaparipalakas. Sri Ponnusamy Thevar of Ramanathapuram Samasthanam took up the effort to publish this work to which Sodashavadanam Subbiraya Chettiyar, a deciple of Tiricirapuram Mahavidvan Meenatchisundaram Pillai has contributed the 'Sirappuppayiram'. In that, he has sung praises of the Sethu described as—'Titara oduum Sethu

Manmiyatthai'. Another poet Kumarasami Pillai has referred to 'Sethumanyamana vadanul thannai'. In the prayer song of Sethu Puranam' the dam built by Sri Rama has been mentioned as "Tuya Seer Ramasethu".

The Sethu's greatness and its sanctity has also been sung of in 64 verses in the chapter 'Sethu Sarukkkam'. The need to built the Sethu for Sri Rama has been explained in Sethu Vanda Sarrukkam'. In 151 verses of the 'Sethu Madhava Sarukkam' and Sethu Yatthirai Sarukkam', are detailed the benefits reaped by merely thinking about the Sethu and taking a holy dip in it. The Tala Puranam (Volume I) in Tamil literature also mentions the 'Sethu puranam'.

It remained a traditional practice of Tamils to give lectures in praise of 'Sethu Puranam'. Arumuga Navalar, who was one among those who did so, has also written it in manuscripts. It was printed and published by Sri M.R.M.S. Ramalinga Pillai of Rameshwaram in the name of 'Sethu Makattuvam' (Rameshwara Manmiyam). This "Sethu Puranaprasangam' which begins with Suta Puran (a narration of the story to Sounakadi Rishis in Naimisaranyanm) is written in the form of a dialogue.

"Anaiyalai Sulkadal Andradainadu Vazhiseithavan" says Thiru Gnana Sambandar in his Tevaram.

Thirunavukkarasar in his Tevaram sings of the construction of the dam by Sri Rama as "Kadalidai Malaikal Tammal Adaittu Mal Karumam Muttri".

All the above references from epics puranas and literature - written in different languages, in different times stand testimony to the fact that the dam 'Sethu' was built as per the orders given by Sri Rama to Nala.

Sethu Nadu:

The Samashthana of Ramanathapuram (Ramnad) was called as 'Sethu Nadu' only because of the very existence of the 'Sethu'. The King of this *samashthana* was known as Sethupati and Sethu Kavalar [*i.e.*Lord of the Cause way]. Thirupullani which is 6 miles southeast of 'Ramnad' is known as Adisethu. Ramayana says Sri Rama appointed people from the Maravar community to protect the 'Sethu' and the people who come to take a holy bath in it.

All the kings of this dynasty are called as ' Sethupati' by the people of successive generations One of the kings of 'Sethupati dynasty' constructed a town near 'Thirupullani'.It was named as "Mugavai" as it stood at the gateway to the 'Sethu'. Later it became Ramanathapuram. It is obvious that the kings of Sethu Nad had long cherished connection with the Sethu. Among them, Adiraghunatha Sethupati, Jeyatunga Raghunatha Sethupathi,Ativeera Rahunatha Sethupati Varaguna Raghunatha Sethupati and six others are mentioned as the earliest kings of the Sethupati dynasty.

The names 'Rahunatha' and 'Sethupati' are attached to them, because of their relationship with Sri Rama [Who is also called Raghunatha] and the dam built by him.. It stands as a clear testimony to the existence of Rama Sethu and also to the point that all the kings of the 'Sethupati' dynasty ruled this area with great devotion and dedication.

RECENT REFERENCES TO RAMA SETU

In 1910 Ramanathapuram district was constituted. The Manual about its political, geographical, industrial, agricultural, economical growth, besides information about population its distribution, transport, revenue, ports, holy places after several revisions was updated in 1968. and was released only in 1972, after making some necessary final changes.

The Foreword to the District Manual of Ramanathapuram was written by the then Chief Minister of Tamilnadu, M. Karunanidhi. He observed:

"The task of collecting and publishing the district manuals was given top priority after independence and was given preference in the five year plans. The District Manual of today is not only a guide furnishing mere information. It is of great help containing several important topics and *can be used very much as a source of great reference. A manual throws light on our age and traditions and long cherished culture.* It serves as mirror which reflects our society. Once having a thorough knowledge of the Manual we can march forward keeping our head high and be proud of our well nurtured culture and traditions"

In the Manual so lauded, the following passage occurs [Box 3] which makes clear the 'tradition' connected with Rama Setu. "Rama Setu has been consistently referred to with pride by various Kings through the ages".

ADAM (-adam, *Hind.*). From (adamah, neb, tawny). Mahomedan patriarchal alam [alam]. Compare: Citrus medica, var. limetta, adam's apple; Musa paradisiaca, adam's fig; Tabernaemontana coronaria, adam's apple; Yucca aloifolia, adam's needle. See gloss. paragraphs.—*Adam's bridge* (- Shéthu, Tam.). *Title from the Mahomedan tradition that Adam on his expulsion from paradise, crossed to Ceylon by this bridge.* Tamul means artificial bund. Tam. also (tiruvanai), meaning holy + bund. Sanscrit name (nalasétu), meaning nalan, the money who constructed the causeway + bund. Also rámaseétu), meaning Rama + bund. Also (ádisétu), meaning first bridge. Isthmus; Madura dist., Rannaud tal.; lat 9°5'; long. 79°30'; from Madura E.S.E. 110 miles; from Ramnaud E.S.E. 48 miles. Narrow ridge of sand and rocks mostly dry, nearly closing the Gulf of Manaar on the nroth and north-east. Western extremity joins the eastern point of Rameshwaram island; eastern extremity joins the eastern point of Manaar island; with these two islands it almost connects Ceylon with the peninsula. *Called the bridge of Rama by Bramins, as along it Rama aided by Hanooman with his host of monkeys marched when invading Ceylon. It really joined Ceylon to Idnai until 1480, when a breach was made through rocks during a storm. A subsequent storm enlarged this and foot traffic then ceased.* Length about 30 miles, breadth 1¼ miles, direction south-east to north-west. Partly above and partly below water; but when covered has now here above three or four feet of water [charitram].—*Adam's needle* (— ádamkisui, Hind.). Title from leaves. Botanically Yucca aloifolia, inn., liliacese [vricsham, 136]. Large plant; common long, hard, flattened leaves, each tipped with a needle-like thorn; white flowers, hanging like bells. Yucca gloriosa, linn, or Spanish bayonet is distinguished from aloifolia by its leaves being much narrower and spikelike.

Source : District Manual of Ramanatha [Reprinted 1972 of 1893 edition]

In *Encyclopedia Brittanica*, it is stated thus: Adam's Bridge also called Rama's Bridge, is a chain of shoals, between the island of Mannar, off northwestern Sri Lanka, and Rameswaram, off the southeastern coast of India. Traditionally, it is said to be the remnant of a huge causeway constructed by Rama, the hero of the Hindu epic Ramayana, to facilitate the passage of his army from India to Ceylon (Sri Lanka) for the rescue of his abducted wife, Sita. According to Muslim legend, Adam crossed there to Adam's Peak, Ceylon, atop which he stood repentant on one foot for 1,000 years. (http://www.britannicaindia.com/duk_det_inside.asp?art_id=28)

According to V. Sundaram IAS (Retd) and currently associate Editor of News Today, a Chennai eveninger, Lord Pentland the then Governor of Madras, in 1914 wrote to the Viceroy Lord Hardinge that "I would earnestly request you to direct the Archeaological Survey India (ASI) to undertake an extensive and intensive survey of Rameswaram and it's beautiful environs, particularly with reference to the historic and primordial Adam's Bridge".

This request was never acted upon. Even after India became free from foreign rule, the Rama Setu continued to be neglected. The Ministry of Culture in 2007 went so far as to deny the need to carry out a survey at all to determine whether the Rama Setu qualified under law to be declared an 'Ancient Monument'. This is another angle of the secret agenda to demolish the Rama Setu.

MODERN RESEARCH

There are of course scientific and other evidence that the Rama Setu is an ancient land-bridge causeway that was constructed and hence should be declared *as a* World Heritage Monument.

NASA in the USA and NRSA of the Ministry of Space, Government of India have published satellite photo images that clearly establish a causeway-like formation between Dhanushkodi in India and Talaimannar island in Srilanka. Of course, NASA is in no position to state whether the formation is natural or constructed. It was wrong for the government to interpret this inability, to claim that it was indeed a natural formation! (see Annexure 6 for the *faux pas*). The bridge is composed of a series of islands and shoals (sand accumulations created by ocean currents). Thus, the entire bridge right from the sea-bed to the surface sea level is a bridge formation which has been recognized for long as a land bridge linking the two regions: Bharat and Srilanka. To what extent there was manual intervention in connecting the gaps between the shoals and islands during the pre-historic periods (as detailed in the ancient texts such as Ramayanam), is a matter for detailed marine archaeological and geological evaluation. The reports of submergence of Kumarikandam, Poompuhar, Dwaraka along the Indian coastline and the formation of the Gulf of Khambat about 10,000 years ago (confirmed by scientists of the National Institute of Ocean Technology) point to the possibility that the recent historical record of submergence of Dhanushkodi island should provide pause and re-evaluation of the impact of the ocean currents and changes in sea-level on the coastline and also on the SSCP. Such a multi-disciplinary archaeological-geological-aquatic environment study should be undertaken which also respects the sentiments of the people who have looked upon the bridge as a land-link between Bharatam and Srilanka. The fact that India is described in the Government seal as *Aasetu himachala paryantam,* the fact that the project itself is called Setusamudram canal project (Setu means bridge), confirms the tradition related to the bridge. Hurting the sentiments of the people who revere Sri Rama as a divinity and personification of dharma, will be a serious breach of trust and will evince utter disdain for peoples' sentiments. In fact, the SSCP should be reconsidered and re-evaluated. The pros-and-cons of reactivating the land bridge between Srilanka and Bharatam should be considered afresh.

Earlier most of the arguments are based on assumptions and partial data obtained from NASA satellite images. No doubt these images are astounding as they bring out the marine geomorphology of the area; but as stated by NASA officials themselves "Remote sensing images from orbit cannot provide direct information about the origin or age of a chain of island, and cannot determine whether humans were involved in producing any of the patterns seen" [see Annexure 6]. According to S. Badrinarayanan, Director (Retd), Geological Survey of India his investigations reveal *that the Rama Setu is not a natural formation but a constructed causeway.* The observations of Dr. Badrinarayanan given above were based purely on hard field work including geological and geophysical surveys coupled with logging and interpretations of several cores and boreholes carried out in the area. A considerable amount of geological information is now available [see Annexure 11].

The climate of the earth has not always been very warm. There have been periods of extreme cold climate that occurred in the geological past wherein most of the surface of the earth was covered with vast quantities of ice and these periods are referred to as Ice Ages. The most recent one occurred during the late Pleistocene age eighteen thousand years before the present. During this period the sea level was lower by about 130m than what it is today. Due to this the land area was extending for far greater distances than what it is today. At that time the Indian subcontinent extended far beyond Sri Lanka. Subsequently due to global warming and other causes there have been periodic rises in sea level, submerging several of these additional areas. About 7300 BP there was a major spurt in sea level rise which resulted in submergence of several areas all over the world.

The Indian side of the land mass adjoining the Ramsetu originates from the southeastern end of the Rameswaram Island at Dhanushkodi. The island itself is a long linear sandy terrain providing calcareous sand stone and occasional coral formation. This area was devastated by a major cyclone in 1956 when part of the area was lost to the sea. The Rameswaram Island connects to the main land through the Pamban area. Further to the west charnocites and granites are exposed.

In order to understand the geology and the structure of the area in the marine domain, several surveys were carried out onboard a research vessel with underwater sensor. These included multibeam echo sounder survey, sub bottom profiler survey, side scan sonar and magnetic survey. The entire area was sampled by deploying vibro core, mainly to the north of the Ramsetu. These surveys generally required at least 4m of water surface so that the equipments are not damaged. The bathymetric survey brought out the fact that the bridge, was a shallow ridge varying in width from 1.6 to 4km. It was shallow and so could not be surveyed. However it was seen from the geological and geophysical surveys that the Bridge is a fault zone rising suddenly from the Bay of Bengal side to the north. This scarp like feature is the shallowest part of the Rama Setu. Even though it is mostly submerged in water there are series of small Islet like features which project above the sea surface. In all about 10 boreholes have been drilled along this ridge up to the international boundary. Out of the ten boreholes, six boreholes were in the sea. The result of the bore logging clearly showed about 1.5m to 4m marine sand followed by 1.5 to 2.5m of boulders of calcareous sand stones and coral followed again by marine sand to various depths end at continuous compact formation.[see Figure 4].

As Dr Badrinarayanan pointed out:

It is a well known fact that the coral reefs can only form in clean and unpolluted water and these being marine organisms required firm and compact formation as foundation. The presence of loose marine sand below these clearly indicates that these are not natural and are transported. Unless somebody has transported and dumped them these could not have come there."

Some of the boulders are so light they could float on water. Apparently whoever has done it has identified light and strong boulders to make for easy transportation. Since the boulders are strong they can withstand a lot of weight.

Corals are present on land in Rameswaram, Pamban and Tuticorin areas. A study of these and dating them clearly show that the age of the coral is about 10,000 years and that the sea level at the time was 4m above the present day sea level. Thereafter there has been a

Figure 4:

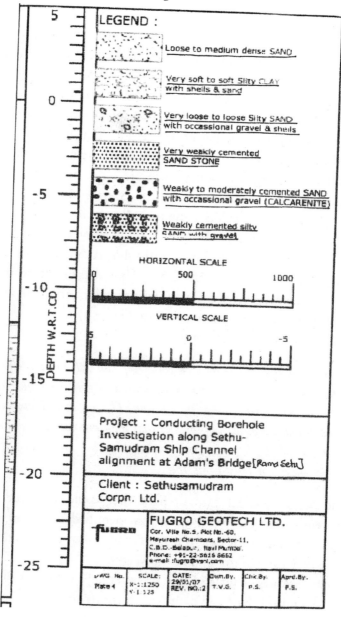

Source: *The Detail Project Report* submitted by L & T Ramboll (2004) & Fugro Geotech (2007).

lowering of sea level; and between 4 to 5 thousand years BP, the sea level was about 1.5m above the present day sea level.

The 1.5 to 2.5m thick zone of corals and rock presently occurring at shallow depths in the sea atop the crustal portion of the Rama Setu appear to be an ancient causeway. The ancients appear to have taken advantage of the crustal portion of the ridge to avoid wastage by dumping of rocks and boulders; and they also utilized less dense but compact rocks and boulders so that these could be carried easily to greater distances and also so that at the same time they were strong enough to withstand pressure from above by human as well as sea forces.

The Rama Setu is a wonderful divide separating the turbulent Bay of Bengal in the north and the calm and tranquil waters of the Gulf of Mannar to the south. Due to this tranquil condition, very rare species of corals and other sea organisms grow in the Gulf of Mannar, whereas these species are completely absent in the Bay of Bengal side. The turbulent tide and the associated sediments caused by the severe cyclones that occur every year in the Bay of Bengal are blocked by the ridge of the Rama Setu which there by protects the fragile conditions in the Gulf of Mannar.

In all likelihood the dredging and opening of the Setu may cause the sediments and turbulent tide to enter the tranquil Gulf of Mannar and choke and destroy the delicate coral islands. As an alternative, dredging in the Pamban or nearby areas and by passing the Rama Setu may be favourably considered, like other inter sea canals e.g., Panama Canal, locks could be provided both in the Palk Bay side and Gulf of Mannar side so that such calamities could be prevented.

Based on this evidence, I wrote to the Ministry of Culture demanding an inquiry; but with mysterious unreasonableness the Minister declined to consider the demand.

Besides Dr. Badrinarayanan, the Earth Sciences Department of the Union Government in an opinion sent on a reference from the then President of India Dr. Abdul Kalam (and reported in the Kolkata

Table 3 Savings in Time

From	To	Existing Route		SSC Route						Savings in Time (hours)
		Distance (NM)	Time @ 12nm (hours)	Distance (NM)	Canal Length (NM)	Time @ 8 nm (hours)	Open Sea (NM)	Time @ 12 nm (hours)	Total Time Required (hours)	
Point A Middle East, Europe	Calcutta	1228.3	102.4	1059.6	82	10.3	977.6	81.5	91.7	10.6
	Vizag	909.9	75.8	693.7	82	10.3	611.7	51.0	61.2	14.6
	Chennai	646.2	53.9	387.3	82	10.3	305.3	25.4	35.7	18.2
Point B Africa	Calcutta	1230.7	102.6	1128.5	82	10.3	1046.5	87.2	97.5	5.1
	Vizag	912.3	76.0	762.6	82	10.3	680.6	56.7	67.0	9.1
	Chennai	648.6	54.0	456.2	82	10.3	374.2	31.2	41.4	12.6
	Average	929.3	77.4	748.0	82.0	10.3	666	55.5	65.7	11.7
							Average Time Saved			11.7
							Less: Pilotage Time			2.0
							Net Savings in Time			9.7

Source: www.kalyan97.wordpress.org.

daily *The Telegraph* of May 8, 2007 – Annexure 4) stated the same view as follows:

"During the glacial Maxima, the sea level was about 130m lower than what is today. This is evidenced both on the east and west coast of India, where submerged Corals occur around 1 to 2m water depths and they are clear indicators of near coastal zone… However, during the last ice age (18,000 year BP) the entire area from India to Sri Lanka and further south and southeast were contiguous land due to the highly lowered sea level. As and when there were major melting of glaciers both from the mountains as well as from the Antarctic area, the sea level was rising. These features were well recorded and studied in several submerged coral formations all over the world. About 7,300 years BP the sea level in the southern part of India was about 3.5 m above the present level. This has been deciphered by Dr. P.K. Banerjee, who studied corals that are found in the land part as at Pamban, Rameswaram, and Tuticorin etc. Subsequently the sea level went down and rose +2m above than what is today between 5000 to 4000 years B.P. In almost of all the boreholes between 4.5 and 7.5m the borehole intersected hard formations, which have been found to be calcareous sand stones and corals. It is to be pointed out here that Corals are comparatively less dense, compact and somewhat easy to carry. The Corals normally grow atop compact to hard formations for the purpose of stability, and as the sea level rises, the Coral colony grows up vertically to maintain water depth of 1 to 2 m, which is essential for their survival. It is always observed that these Corals have continuous vertical growth like Lakshadweep, Andaman's, and Gulf of Mannar Natural Park. These have always been found to grow on hard rock bottom. In the case of Adams bridge area we observe that the Coral formations hardly occur 1 to 2.5m in length and resting on loose marine sands. Most of these coral rock pieces seem to be rounded pebbles of corals. *These things appear to point these coral rock pieces and pebbles have been transported and placed in these areas.* Since the calcareous sand stones and Corals are less dense than normal hard rock and quite compact, probably these were used by the ancients to form a connecting link to Sri Lanka, on the higher elevations of the Adams bridge ridge and this is analogous to modern day causeway. In support of these observations there are many archaeological and geoarchaeological evidences on the south east coast of India around Rameswaram, Tuticorin and the western coast of Sri Lanka. There are raised Teri formations that supported a rich assemblage of mesolithic – microlithic tools indicating the presence of strong human habitation and activity in these areas as early as 8000 to 9000 years B.P. and as recent as 4000 years B.P. On Sri Lanka side there are indications of human habitation extending to late Pleistocene (about 13,000 B.P.) based on bone and fossils of human and animal form. All these point to a flourishing human activity on both side of Adams Bridge and probably when the sea levels were just right the link between India and Sri Lanka could have been established."

Eminent Archeologist former DG ASI Dr. S.R. Rao also wrote to the Union Minister of Shipping to opine that the Rama Setu was constructed and not a natural formation (Annexure 7).

Thus the Tamil Nadu Chief Minister Mr. Karunanidhi and his lieutenant & Union Shipping Minister Mr. T.R. Baalu have been telling outright lies to the public about the non existence of evidence on the Rama Setu, and as we shall see later, on the economic and environmental viability of the Sethusamudram Shipping Channel Project (SSCP).

While Mr. Karunanidhi in his speeches has debunked the Setu and Rama, the DMK State Government and the UPA Union Governments have been advertising and affirming the exact opposite: existence of the Setu and the historicity of Rama! For example, the Tourism Department of the Tamil Nadu Government has been advertising in railway trains, urging the people to visit Rameshwaram and see where Rama set his "lotus feet", to build a bridge (Setu) to Sri Lanka with the help of the Vanar Sena (see enclosed photo), to rescue his wife Sita.

The National Remote Sensing Agency (NRSA), of the Union Ministry of Space has published a book of satellite photographs [ISBN: 817525 6524] claiming that "archeological studies show" that the Setu "may be man made" on the cover of this study. This book has been distributed to all MPs free by the Ministry of Space. Yet on August 14, 2007 in the Rajya Sabha, in reply to a question Ms Ambika Soni as Minister of Culture falsely stated that "no archeological studies has been made in respect of the Rama Setu". This is a breach of privilege of the House, for which she should be punished.

The Ministry has also suppressed the above mentioned report prepared by Dr S Badrinarayanan, former Director of Geological Survey of India (GSI) which is based on a 2002 investigation under the sea near and at the Setu. The Report concluded that Rama Setu had been constructed, at least 9000 years ago, and is not a natural formation as claimed by Mr. Karunanidhi. However without consulting the GSI, the Ministry of Culture hastily filed an affidavit in the Supreme Court that "there is no information or studies in the knowledge of the Government that Rama Setu is man made". Thereafter, on public outcry, it had to eat humble pie and withdraw the affidavit. As stated earlier former ASI DG SR Rao has also ridiculed this stand of the Government (see enclosed letter; Annexure 7).

The SSCP is also an economic loss, an environmental disaster, a national security risk, and productive of monumental corruption. As we shall see in a subsequent Chapter, the Ministry of Environment & Forests had (in a letter dated April 8, 1999 to the Ministry of Surface Transport), conveyed it's opinion that the SSCP should be scrapped as it is an environmental disaster (see Annexure 5). This opinion was based on an analysis of the NEERI Report of 1998. Yet in 2004 the Ministry reversed it's opinion based on the same 1998 data. Why? No explanation has been given so far for this somersault a further indication of *malafide*.

It is a grave conflict of interest for the Union Shipping Minister TR Baalu to pursue this project since he owns a shipping company, with ships of less than 30,000 DWT. It may also enable dredging companies such as T.R.B. Selvam & Co (TR Baalu's son's company) to earn money and help LTTE to move it's terrorist and narcotic base to the Kerala Coast. Therefore this anti-national project should be scrapped if no other alternative route, except by breaking Rama Setu, is acceptable to Karunanidhi.

CHAPTER 4

Economic Viability of the Project

It is my submission in this chapter that a proper and correct calculation of costs and benefits suggests that the Sethusamudrum Ship Canal Project (SSCP) is a 'financial white elephant'. The central premise of the Project is that, since ships will no longer have to navigate around Sri Lanka (Figure 5), it will reduce travel time on sea between Tuticorin (Thuthukudi) port and the ports of the east coast of India. The crux of the profitability argument in favour of the Project, is that ships from the west coast of India to the east coast, not having to therefore circumbulate Sri Lanka, would save time, fuel and other costs, by traveling through the proposed channel,. Hence the internal rate of return is estimated at 10-15 percent on investment, on a present value of estimated revenues and costs. Hence the argument that the government invest in the Project.

The Detailed Project Report prepared by Larsen and Toubro Ramboll (DPR) calculated distance savings for ships using Tuticorin and Kanyakumari as starting points. The average distance and time saved, as calculated in the DPR, are 335 nautical miles and 30 hours respectively. But ships from other further away starting points cannot save 30 hours or 335 nautical miles. For example, ships from Europe, the Middle East and Africa will save much less time than ships moving from the east coast to the west coast of India. This is because ships on an open sea voyage will travel at 12-14 knots per hour, while through the Channel the speed will have to be reduced to less than half that. At the current tariff levels proposed in the SSCP, ships will in fact therefore find it cheaper to travel around Sri Lanka rather than use the Sethusamudram Channel!

Figure 5

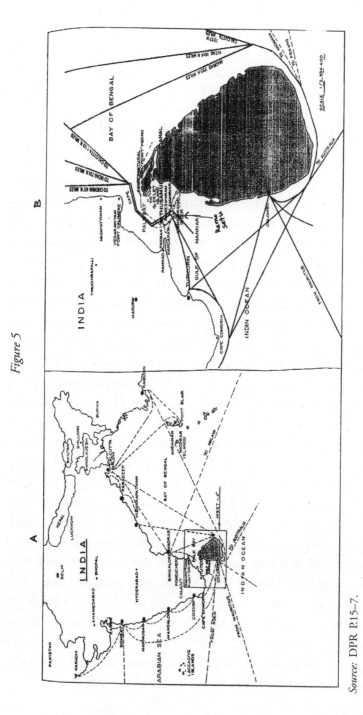

Fig. 1 Index Plan of Proposed Sethusamudram Ship Channel

Source: DPR P15–7.

The Project's profitability is also contingent on chosen interest rates. The DPR assumes a much lower interest rate than the current market rates: thus significantly understating loan repayment costs and therefore the total costs of the channel. Accurate market rate of interests would of course lower the internal rate of return, as we shall see presently.

The usual way to calculate the economic viability of a project is to estimate the revenues over time, as well as the fixed and variable costs of the project. The net benefit to ships is calculated on the assumption of the tariff to be paid by a ship at the proposed rates, and then set against this, the costs saved by taking a shorter route via the channel. However, in the case of the Sethusamudram Ship Canal Project {SSCP}, without the requisite careful testing of data, the Government of India rushed into implementing it. Since the revenue and cost have not been properly estimated or carefully calculated, what is now required is an informed and manysided national debate. Moreover, the now proposed 167 km long Sethusamudram Shipping Channel, which is actually a furrow in the seabed created by dredging the ocean floor to a depth of 12 meters and a width of 300 meters, can structurally allow passage of ships only of 30,000 DWT in weight or less. But in fact, today most ships are of more than 60,000 DWT and thus they cannot use the channel at all! *And yet, the DPR is premised on 3000 or more ships passing through the channel per year.* The Union shipping Minister TR Baalu gives an even larger, and wilder figure to 16,000 ships! Currently, in a year, only about 250 or less ships dock at Tuticorin port and then proceed around Sri Lanka to Chennai, Vishakapatnam, Kolkata, and other ports eastwards.

The UPA government does not seem to have bothered to study the financial (and also environmental implications) of the SSCP, before rushing in on July 2, 2005 to inaugurate the works on the Rs. 2,427-crore project. The project is now entangled in a challenge in the Supreme Court, on Writ Petitions filed by this author and others, and a stay or injunction has been granted against proceeding to dredge through the Rama Setu.

While for the ruling Congress Party, the biggest public embarrassment in the implementation of the project, is the public opposition to the proposed channel alignment which requires blasting a 300 metre cavity through the Rama Setu (the partially undersea causeway between the Palk Bay and the Gulf of Mannar), there are (besides the issue of economic viability) other substantive objections as well. The project is environmentally non-sustainable— in fact hazardous— besides being a financial disaster that will continuously guzzle resources on maintenance. Hence it is altogether unviable. Moreover the operation of the channel will close down fishing activities of the poor coastal fishermen; and it also threatens India's national security by facilitating LTTE terrorists, drug peddlers and smugglers easy passage south of the Rama Setu to Tuticorin and Kanyakumari.

The objectionable Alignment No. 6 channel route was chosen from six possible alignments that have been suggested from time to time between 1860 and 2004. It involves cutting through Rama Setu. Interestingly, all the other five Alignments suggested earlier, before or after Independence, called for skirting the Rama Setu and instead required cutting through land, either on the mainland at Mandappam, or through Pambam Island (Table 1).

The Suez and the Panama canals, which handle modern ships of heavy dead weight, were dug through land mass and, therefore, stay dug and free of fresh sand sediments from seawaves. That is not the case with the Sethusamudram Channel which will need constant dredging to keep shifting sands, moved by currents, out of the dug-out trough or furrow, thus imposing heavy recurrent maintenance cost. The side walls of the channels moreover cannot be lined or protected by any artificial material, because the channel is furrowed under water. Hence, a strong tidal wave is enough to level the channel that had been laboriously dredged at a heavy cost to the nation.

Despite these factors, the proponents of the Sethusamudram Ship canal Project hold that the Project is economically justified, despite these factors, by blandly stating that the channel, if used, would save up to 30 hours of shipping time. However, the detailed project report (DPR) itself states that the biggest saving (a maximum of 30 hours) will only be for journeys from Tuticorin to Chennai. Recently many naval experts, notably retired Captain H. Balakrishnan, have calculated that, with the exception of voyages from ports on the Indian west coast to ports on the Indian east coast, there are unlikely to be any significant gains in terms of time saved for other ships that are making the voyage through the Sethusamudram channel.

Surprisingly, this information is not reflected in the L & T Ramboll prepared DPR which assumed that voyage time saved for all ships *will be the same whether they start at Tuticorin or not!* Without this absurd assumption, the project cannot be shown to be profitable. Only a few ships however originate from Indian coastal ports: in fact not more than 250 of the 3000 plus claimed traffic do so. For ships coming from places like Europe and Africa, the average savings is at most 10 hours and certainly nowhere near the flat 30 hours assumed in the DPR (see Table 3). A journey for an eligible ship (i.e. less than 30,000 DWT) from Mauritius to Kolkata, for example, *would actually be longer by nearly three and a half hours for an average ship* (Figure 6 & Table 4 below).

Figure 6 Comparison of Savings for Coastal/Non-Coastal Ships (20,000 SWT Ships, in $)

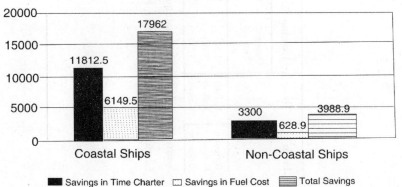

Table 4 Calculating Time Saved

From	To	Existing Route			SSC Route						Savings in Time (Hours including Two Hours for Pilotage)
		Distance (nm)	Time @ 12nm (Hours)	Distance *nm)	Canal Length (nm)	Time@ 8nm (Hours)	Open Sea (nm)	Time @ 12 nm (Hours)	Total Time Required (Hours)	
Tuticorin	Kolkata	1371	114.3	1041.0	82	10.3	959	79.9	90.2	22.1
Europe	Kolkata	3301	275	3135	82	10.3	3053	254.4	264.7	8.4
Africa	Kolkata	3217	268	3194	82	10.3	3112	259.3	269.6	-3.5

Source : John, Jacob: "Sethusamudram Canal : An Expensive Voyage"

Economic and Political Weekly, Kuly 21, 2007 p. 2993.

Hence the average savings for a ship of 30,000 DWT or less, making a voyage from either Europe or Africa works out to just $3,989, which is only 22% of the savings projected in the DPR. At the proposed tariff structure for ships from Africa and Europe, using the channel would mean *actually making a loss* of $4,992 on every voyage. In this scenario, the *pre-tax* IRR (internal rate of return) on investment in SSCP, (contrary to the claimed 10 percent), falls to just 2.6%! This is a very low return, a level at which public infrastructure projects are usually rejected by the Government. This rate of return is also based on an assumption that per year more than 3000 ships will use the SSCP route— for which assumption there is no credible basis. Indeed the London-based International Shipping Association rejects this level of traffic for the SSCP.

As stated above, the favoured size of merchant ships today is of 60,000 DWT and above, thus making the proposed channel unusable by most ships. Hence, the estimate of 3000 or more ships using the channel is quite unrealistic.

The basic assumption— that the SSCP will reduce fuel cost and sailing time for ships— is not therefore based on hard facts. Of course, the sailing distance of ships docking en route at Tuticorin will be reduced by about 375 nautical miles :such ships can avoid circumnavigating Sri Lanka in the outward journey to other east coast ports such as Kolkata. But to navigate the 167 km stretch of the SSC, ships on routes other than the west coast – east coast route, will end up spending more time than by going around Sri Lanka. This is because before entering the SSC, a ship will first have to start slowing down about 2 hours before reaching the mouth of the channel. Then, it will follow several pre-ordained procedures from dropping anchor to waiting for a pilot to board the ship to steer it through the fragile channel at half its open sea route speed. All this will consume about 15 hours.

Furthermore, between October to December every year, the cyclonic storms and winter monsoon will make the channel unusable. How many shipping companies will be willing to undergo all these formalities and provide as well for the vagaries of nature?

It may be borne in mind that the SSCP is not an 'open seaway'. Thus, for ships to safely traverse through the channel, it will be mandatory to contract a 'pilot'. A 'pilot' is a mariner with experience pertaining to local conditions. The pilot would normally board a vessel at either extremity of the channel and supervise the tugging of the vessel safely to the other extremity. It is not clear at the present juncture, whether vessels calling at the SSCP will actually have a pilot available to board immediately on arrival. Delays in the boarding of the pilot will entail the vessel having to anchor and await the 'pilot'. Under adverse weather conditions this is not a comforting thought to a ship captain. Besides, during cyclonic weather, sea conditions may preclude the embarkation of a 'pilot'. What does the vessel then do? No answers are found in the DPR.

4.1 Distance saved

A core claim of the proponents of the SSCP is that it will significantly cut the distance traveled, and hence the cost of fuel and time, for journeys from the east coast to the west coast of India. Thus, this assured savings in fuel and time, will encourage ships to use the channel. The officials of the project have publicly been claiming that the journey time will be reduced by 36 hours and the distance by 400 nautical miles. Firstly, there seems to be confusion *on the actual time* that will be saved by ships using this channel. The DPR claims a maximum of 30 hours saved. For the purposes of this study, we use the average figure of 22.5 hours {L&T-Ramboll DPR p.15-3}.

The L&T-Ramboll DPR calculates distance and fuel saved by using an average of the distance saved from Kanyakumari and Tuticorin to Chennai, Vishakapatnam and Calcutta. Using the distances saved from these points, an average figure of 335 nautical miles is calculated as shown in Table 5 below:

Table 5. Savings in Distance Due to SSCP

From	To	Existing Route	SSC, Route	Savings in Distance
Kanyakumari	Chennai	755	407	348
	Vishakapatnam	1014	724	290
	Kolkatta	1357	1103	254
Tuticorin	Chennai	769	345	424
	Vishakapatnam	1028	662	366
	Kolkatta	1371	1041	330
			Average	335.3

Source: L&T Ramboll DPR, p.15-1

Note: The distances saved, stated in NM (Nautical Miles) are measured from points Kanyakumari and Tuticorin and would be applicable for coastal cargo.

The omission in this calculation for *non-coastal* cargo is very significant as the omission substantially overstates the total savings in journey time. As non-coastal cargo ships form an overwhelming majority of the projected SSCP users (around 65%), we need to consider if it will be economic or sensible for them to use this channel at all. That the L&T-Ramboll DPR does not consider savings of time across different origin-destination pairs, thereby severely vitiating its analysis especially since the project is justified by the SPV to traders on the basis of cutting down travel time from Africa, the Middle East and Europe to the east coast of India.

4.2 Time Saved

It is important to note that while the shipping lane or channel does reduce distance, it does not always reduce the time taken for the journey in a proportionate manner. This is because, within the channel, ships will operate at a restricted speed of 6 knots per hour. This will be significantly lower than their optimal speed of around 12-13 knots.

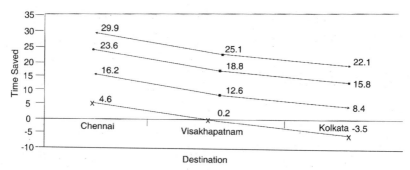

Source: DPR p. 15-3 and *John, Jacob*: "The Sethusamudram Canal" *Economic & Political Weekly*, Mumbai, July 21, 2007.

Figure 7: Time saved for different origin destination pairs (in hours)

Using a calculation similar to that used in the L&T-Ramboll DPR, the savings in time for ships arriving from Africa can be as low as 5 hours –which is negligible on a voyage that takes many days. Table 3 above gives the details on which Figure 10 has been drawn:

Table 3 gives the time saved across all the voyages given in the L&T-Ramboll DPR and arrives at the average figure. The greatest time that is saved (for journeys to Chennai from the Middle East/ Europe) is 18 hours and not 30 hours. On the average the net savings in time after accounting for pilotage is just around 10 hours: one third of what is claimed in the L&T-Ramboll DPR. (See L&T-Ramboll DPR p.15-3).

Thus the savings in time charter rates are just 43% of what is stated in the L&T-Ramboll DPR. It needs clarification here that the dramatic reduction in savings for some coastal traffic ships does not mean that the savings can be significant for non-coast-to-coast cargo. The point that this paper makes is that coast-to-coast cargo will mean that the SSCP will be an economically unviable project since most of its revenues in DPR are to be obtained from non-coastal sources.

4.3 Fuel Saved

One of the principle arguments in favour of the SSCP is that a shorter distance can result in significant fuel savings. The use of the Sethusamudram channel, implying a decrease in distance, does not however necessarily mean it will reduce fuel consumption. The DPR highlights that for travel at lower speeds, a better quality fuel is required. (DPR, p.15-2) because first, a lower quality fuel at lower speeds results in increased carbon deposition in the engines, causing greater damage. Hence the need to use a lighter but more expensive fuel that is less damaging to the engines. Secondly, environmental norms require that low sulphur diesel be used for voyages that go through ecologically sensitive areas. This fuel is also more expensive.

The SSCP's DPR thus underestimates the total fuel cost as it does not account for the use of low sulphur diesel in the ecologically sensitive Palk Bay Biosphere reserve area. In fact, there is no mention at all of low sulphur diesel that should be used in these areas. Our estimates for fuel savings are therefore extracted from the L&T-Ramboll DPR, which simply states that, the "ships will use IFO in the open seas and MDO in the channel where there is a restriction, and a need for a better vehicle response". Neither of the abbreviations is clarified in the L&T-Ramboll DPR, and our usage therefore is based on the information in the DPR only. In Table 5, we simply use the calculation that has already been used in the L&T-Ramboll DPR to calculate savings using the existing routes for Europe and Africa compared to the potential savings by using the channel. Fuel consumption rates and cost of fuel are taken at the same rate as provided in the DPR.

Table 6: Fuel Savings

S. No.	Dead Weight Tonnage (DWT)		
	10000	20000	30000
1. Fuel Consumption kg/km)	19.9	29.2	36.6
2. Existing Route			
a. Distance (NM)	929.3	929.3	929.3
b. Distance (km)	1721	1721	1721
c. Fuel Consumption (kg) = Distance (km) × Fuel consumption (kg/km)	34251	50257	62993
d. Fuel Rate ($ per 1000 kg)*	180	180	180
e. Fuel Consumption ($) = Fuel consumption (kg)* Fuel Rate ($ per 1000 kg)/1000	6165.1	9046.3	11338.8

3. Canal Route			
a. Canal Distance (NM)	82	82	82
b. Canal Distance (km)	152	152	152
c. Fuel Consumption (kg)	3022.1	4434.4	5558.2
d. Fuel Rate ($)*	350	350	350
e. Fuel Consumption ($)	1057.7	1552.1	1945.4
f. Open Sea (NM)	847.3	847.3	847.3]
g. Open Sea (km)	1569.3	1569.3	1569.3
h. Fuel Consumption (kg)	31228.5	45822.7	57435.3
i. Fuel Rate ($)*	180	180	180
j. Fuel Consumption ($)	5621.1	8248.1	10338.3
Total Fuel Cons.($)	6678.9	9800.1	12283.7
Savings in Fuel Cost ($)	–513.8	–753.9	–944.9

* Fuel rate calculations taken from the L&T-Ramboll [DPR p 15-2].

Thus, it is incorrect to state that there will be a substantial saving in fuel costs by using the Sethusamudram Channel. On the contrary, there will be a substantial loss of $500 to $950 depending on the tonnage of the ship.

4.4 Cost-Benefit Analysis of the SSCP

The official project paper of the SSCP states that the estimated investment of about Rs. 2400 crores will "earn an operating profit from its very first year of operation and that the capital will be recovered with 9% interest within the first 25 years after which there will be a mammoth profit".

The capital cost of constructing the SSC is Rs. 2330 crores. The equity component is Rs. 971 crores while the debt portion has been pegged at Rs. 1456.40 crores.

For the debt portion of Rs. 1456.40 crores, assuming an interest burden of 10%, it works out to Rs. 145.64 crores per annum. Assuming a repayment period of 25 years, the annual installments for repaying the capital, work out to Rs. 58.25 crores.

Thus, the total annual financial repayment for servicing the debt would be Rs. 145.64 + Rs. 58.25 crores = Rs. 203.89 crores or Rs. 204 crores (approx).

According to the consultants for the SSCP, the number of ships that are expected to navigate through the SSC is 3055 in 2008 and will rise to 7141 in 2025. Which categories of ships, i.e. by the freight content, are likely to use the Channel? Let us assume as follows:

Coal ships: one can predict that coal-carrying bulk-carriers will navigate through the SSC, which vessels will carry thermal coal from Haldia/Paradeep/Vizag to Chennai/Tuticorin to cater to the requirements of the Thermal Power Plants located at these ports.

Now, what will be the annual requirement of coal ships for Tuticorin? According to former Naval Captain H. Balakrishnan, it can be estimated as follows:

(a) Installed capacity of the Tuticorin Thermal Power plant = 1050 MW,

(b) Annual requirement of coal = 1050 x 6144.8 Tonnes = 6452040 Tonnes. (The figure of 6144.8 Tonnes is the annual requirement of coal to generate 1 MW of power (TNEB website)).

(c) Deadweight Tonnage of a bulk carrier= 30,000 DWT. Thus, number of vessels required annually = 64,52,040/30,000 = 215 ships.

Even at a very optimistic estimate, the number of other vessels to cater to the requirement of petroleum products for Tuticorin and near by areas would amount to 200. For other exports/imports from Tuticorin, an analysis is given herein below on pages 75 to 79 of this chapter.

Thus at best it may be possible that 200+215, or let us say optimistically 500 vessels will use the SSC annually, which is nowhere near the projected 3055 vessels targeted for 2008. This is on account of the fact that global shipping trends are towards using larger vessels of 60,000 DWT and above, and the SSC is restricted to vessels of 30,000 DWT, with a draught limitation of 10.7 Metres. The confirmation of this pessimistic scenario comes from the fact that an open invitation by the SSCP Corporation headquartered in Tuticorin, to international shipping companies to book the channel transit in advance, at lower concessional rates has drawn a blank so far!

Thus, in summary:

(a) The annual financial repayment burden on the SSCP = Rs. 204 crores.

(b) Maximum number of ships expected to use the SSC = 500 ships.

(c) Cost per ship to be levied to break even through pilotage/allied rates =Rs. 204/500 = Rs. 0.4 crores or rupees forty lakhs and forty thousand!!

Based on Table 2 for time saved, and factoring in the fuel and distance costs and savings, and using Captain Balakrishnan data sheets as modified by V. Sundaram [IAS (Retd) and also former Tuticorin Port Trust Chairman], I have re-calculated the DPR numbers to obtain the following startling economics of SSCP, *disproving the claim of the Government that the SSCP will be cost-effective:*

(1)　Kolkata to Tuticorin
    (a)　Circumnavigating Shri Lanka　-　Rs. 19,49,925.00
    (b)　Through the SS Canal　　　　-　Rs. 19,51,126.00
(2)　Chennai to Tuticorin
    (a)　Circumnavigating Shri Lanka　-　Rs. 13,25,405.00
    (b)　Through the SS Canal　　　　-　Rs. 14,51,260.00

In fact, SSCP is not cost-effective or economically viable on the most optimistic of scenarios. It is a financial disaster waiting to happen! A detailed calculation for ships that are to come from abroad is as follows:

Cost Effectiveness:

It had earlier been appreciated that for the Sethusamudram Corporation to 'break even', the 'pilotage rates' that would be charged for every ship availing of the SSC, even at a very conservative estimate, would be Rupees Forty Lakhs and Eighty Thousand in

U.S. dollar terms this works out to $55,979.64 (at an exchange rate of $1=Rs. 39.30 as on 22 October, 2007), and for a Kolkata-Tuticorin trip, this works out as follows:

1. Vessels use of Heavy Fuel Oil (HFO). The cost of 1 Metric Tonne (MT) of HFO as per prevailing price at Singapore on 19 Oct 2007=$462/M.T=Rs. 24,020 per MT.

2. Voyage Kolkata to Tuticorin
   (a) Distance Kolkata-Tuticorin around Sri Lanka = 1227 nm
   (b) Distance Kolkata-Tuticorin via SSCP   = 1098 nm
   (c) Time taken at 12 knots for (a) above   = 102.25 h
   (d) Time taken at 12 and 6 knots for (b) above = 98.5 h

3. *Fuel consumption rate for these vessels* @ 1 MT per hour
   Total voyage fuel consumption will be as follows:
   (a) For Para 2(c)   =   102.25 MT
   (b) For Para 2(d)   =   98.5 MT

4. Hence, *total voyage fuel costs will be as follows:*
   (a) For Para 3(a) above = Rs. 24,020 x 102.5 = Rs. 24,56,045.00
   (b) For Para 3(b) above = Rs. 24,020 x 98.50 = Rs. 23,65,970.00

5. *Total voyage costs including pilotage and allied costs.* (In addition to the foregoing, pilotage and other allied charges as calculated above, have to be added to the values at Para 4(b)). Thus, the total costs will work out as follows:
   Rs. 23,65,970.00 + Rs. 20,40,000.00   = Rs. 44,05,970.00
   This completely turns upside down the cost effectiveness of using the channel. Thus the arbitrary assumption of 3000 plus ship traffic through the channel instead of the realistic number of 500 is crucial for arriving at the cost-effectiveness of the project. This is where the Union Shipping Ministry has fudged the data and claimed profitability of the SSCP.

6. In the same manner, following the above methodology, Capt. Balakrishnan has worked out the cost benefit analysis for a voyage from Muscat to Chittagong around Sri Lanka and via SSCP, and he comes to the following conclusion: Voyage-

Muscat to Chittagong around Sri Lanka is "more cost effective" than routing through the SSC by amounts ranging from $50,943.80 to $51,636.84.

The foregoing calculations clearly highlight the economic non-viability of the SSCP for ships. The earlier analysis had also brought out the same results for vessels involved in Indian coastal trade. Hence it is safe to conclude that the SSCP will only lead to a drain of crores of rupees on the public exchequer, without any benefit or advantage to the nation.

Why SSCP is Not Cost-Effective:

The lack of cost-effectiveness for any route via the SSCP route, is because:

(1) *Firstly*, since the ship cannot be towed at its normal speed through the channel, and time will also be lost in embarkation/disembarkation of pilots and other inspection procedures, the saving in sailing time for ships will be substantially less than the 30 hours projected by the SSCP. Even the saving in sailing time of just about a day will not justify the incurring of over 8 times the cost of the saved fuel;

(2) *Secondly*, ships using the channel, will save money only if SSCP is rendered a financial loser, and viceversa. That is, SSCP will be financially profitable only if commercial ships agree to lose money on tariff paid for using the channel (which is an absurd premise).

It is quite possible that Indian Flag flying ships may be coerced into using the SSC to justify its existence. However, no such compulsion is effective in respect of foreign flag ships.

That is why Capt. Balakrishnan told the Government Committee that the Sethusamudram Canal Project just does not make 'nautical sense'. I challenge the Government and its pliant intellectuals to provide serious alternative scenarios that are feasible and yet make SSCP cost-effective.

While the SSCP does conduct oblique sensitivity analysis {L&T Detailed Project Report p.17-7} to highlight the likely effects of different scenarios, it does not do so for the possible global increases in interest rates which are already at almost double the rates assumed in the project document. The cost of finance of the project is thus underestimated, given the higher level of interest rates today (around 8% for a dollar loan v/s 4.25% in the project document). This means that the interest rate for the foreign currency loan assumed in the DPR is just half of what is the current lending rate.

The total amount that has to be borrowed in foreign currency is the dollar equivalent of Rs. 4,666 and 2,616 million rupees, to be borrowed in June 2007 and 2008 respectively. When the cost of credit for both the Indian rupee and the foreign currency loan are factored in, the cost of the project goes up dramatically. The viability of the Project then becomes an even bigger question mark! Given the shaky basis on which the tariffs are structured the question therefore is whether the project will be financially sustainable.

4.5 Other Issues

There are some other issues that have to be considered with regard to the Sethusamudram project. This includes the fact that a large percentage of cargo that is likely to pass through the canal will be petroleum oil and lubricants (POL). Much of this cargo moves from Mumbai to Vishakapatnam or Haldia or originates from Africa and moves to the eastern coast. Two additional factors could make this set of cargo irrelevant for ships visiting Indian ports. The first is the increasing number of oil pipelines that have been built across the country, which could transport petroleum products across the country through pipelines. The second is the discovery of oils and gas fields across the Godavari basin and off shore along the eastern coast of India. This could actually further reduce the ship traffic that might use the Sethusamudram canal.

Other issues that need to be considered include the risk tolerance of companies that use the channel and the price at which they will decide to use the channel. As the risks of using a closed channel are higher, the tariffs and the cost of using it must fall enough before a shipping company decides to use the channel. It is not clear in the L&T-Ramboll DPR as to what insurance amount is premised in the financial statements and whether it will cover any losses by ships that get stranded in the channel or on the way to it— especially since the PNI Club (which determines insurance rates for the worldwide shipping establishment) has decided not to offer insurance coverage for ships going through the channel. [The PNI Club, based in the U.K., is the only company offering insurance through marine surveyors, which would give coverage to ships either damaged or stuck up in mid sea or which have been grounded on shore or which have caught fire etc. The PNI Club has offices in all countries, including India (at Mumbai); and only after considering all safety aspects, would it have agreed to give insurance coverage for ships passing through the channel. (see PNI Club Website)]. If no such insurance coverage is available for using the channel, naturally ship owners would not use the channel.

The viability of the project thus rests on a set of assumptions that are fundamentally flawed. It assumes that the saving resultant from using the channel, is the same for all ships, when actually it is very different. In fact, the stated public purpose of a reduction in shipping time is not valid for most of the ships using the channel; revenue and time saved have been vastly over-estimated and costs of dredging and maintenance, grossly under-estimated (as the chart below shows).

Incidentally, not only is the SSCP not viable economically, but also thousands of fishermen living in the coastal districts of Tuticorin, Ramanathapuram and Pudukkottai will be deprived of their livelihood Besides, its impact on the fragile ecology of the Gulf of Mannar will be disastrous. According to a report in *Business Line* (on October 16, 2007), the Shipowners Associations have made it clear to the Government that the SSCP and fishing activities *are mutually exclusive.* Hence, *the nation has to choose one or the other:* fishing or the channel utilization for ships. Fishermen have not been told this yet. When they find out, one can imagine the upheaval, anger and anguish in the coastal regions of Tamil Nadu.

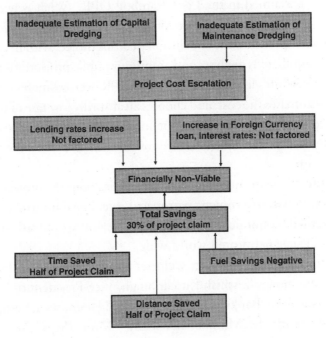

Fig. 8 Diagrammatic representation of factors affecting economic viability of the SSCP

The SSCP has been justified on the basis of the cost savings estimates for ships using the channel. Not only have the cost savings not been set out in adequate detail, but also the actual savings for ships using the channel have been grossly exaggerated. This is especially true for ships coming from Europe/Africa and other such locations. The fuel savings for many of these ships is in fact negative, while the total savings (including reduction in time charter) actually works out to just 30% of what is claimed by the L&T-Ramboll DPR for most non-coastal ships. The factors affecting the economic viability of the SSCP are given in Tabular form below.

The significant lower level of savings implies that the tariff that can be charged by SSCP will be much lower than that claimed by the L&T-Ramboll DPR. This has significant revenue implications as over 60% of the ships which 'benefit' will not be willing to pay the amount as claimed in the L&T-Ramboll DPR. What is needed is greater study of economic benefits as per the present justification. This review points to the conclusion that this project with its current design, injudicious analyses and ambitious public projections will be a financial white elephant. In short, the DPR over-estimates revenue, under-estimates the cost, and chooses an absurdly low rate of interest to discount the net benefits to obtain a high percent value to justify the project. We cannot allow the Government to befool the public in this way.

Despite the hype in a section of the media about the project (hype induced under government patronage), the above information are the essential economic non-viability and lack of cost-effectiveness of the SSCP, has permeated world wide.

"I don't think this project will ever see the light of day because there is no money", Ashish Kumar Singh, Vice-President of Capital Markets at Axis Bank Ltd. told Priyanka Narain, an investigative journalist with the Mumbai newsdaily ' Mint' (Sept. 24, 2007). Axis, formerly known as UTI Bank, was appointed "loan arranger" for the project in 2005, and hence no one would know better.

Since the project's inception in 2004, costs have skyrocketed to at least Rs. 4,000 crore, interest rates have crawled higher and old loan terms have lapsed. Mr. Singh also told Ms. Narain that the project is languishing because "no company will dredge the channel for cheap and Indian dredging companies don't have the required equipment."

Even before the first dredger began its work in 2005, costs had already spiraled to more than Rs. 3,500 crore, Mr. Singh said. The loan sanctions, valid only up to Rs. 2,400 crore, have lapsed. "*To secure more money,*" Mr. Singh said, "*Sethusamudram Corp. Ltd.*

Map showing Sethu built by Sri Rama (within circle).

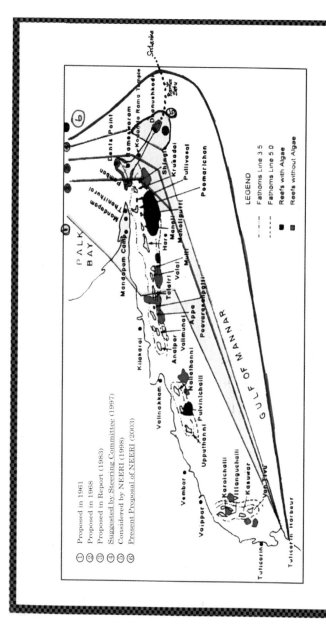

Various Alignments of Sethusamudram Ship Channel Project including the Proposed Alignments.

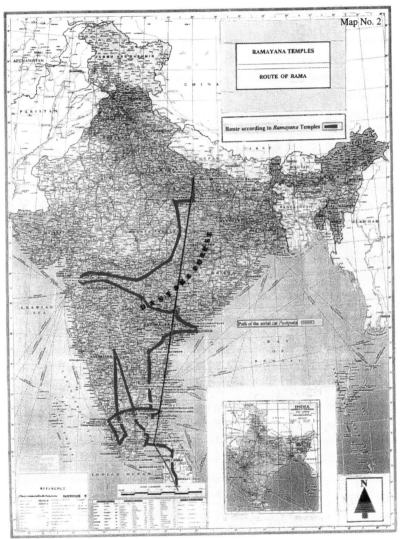

Route of Rama: Route according to Ramayana Temples.

Advertisement by Government of Tamilnadu in the Train Jan Shatabdi Express—Delhi to Dehradun.

Chairman of the Expert Committee on SSCP, Dr. R. Ramachandran, bowing before Tamil Nadu CM, Mr. Karunanidhi, at a protest demonstration against Supreme Court Stay Order on demolition of the Rama Setu held on October 1, 2007.
Source: The Hindu, October 2, 2007.

would have to return to the drawing board, draw up new reports, sit with parliamentary committees and receive fresh approval".

So far, the nodal agency, the Tuticorin Port Trust has not gone back to the government, as the causes of delays in the project have moved from insufficient funds into other, more complicated political arenas in which today it is badly entangled.

Significantly, Mr. Singh, whose bank continues to be the loan arranger for the project, says the government has not approached him to raise any new loans. Even if it did, a government guarantee is now unlikely. "As a stand alone project, no lender will touch this project. First, the interest rates have gone up. It is not possible to lock in the rates. The expected net returns (on proper costing methods even accepting the DPR data) on the project were as low as 7.7% to begin with," he said. "With higher debt cost and higher debt requirements, how can it hope to even break even?"

Not so long ago, before protest defined the future of the Rama Sethu, the project had been based on promises to shorten shipping routes and thus help revive Tamil Nadu's economy. In late 2005, Axis had little problem selling the idea to lenders. When the bank hit the road to drum up interest, "it was the most attractive thing out there,' Singh, who managed the loan-raising process for Sethusamudram, told Ms. Narain. "It had great visibility, people were excited....and there was a buzz around it."

While the Union government and other government organizations, such as the Tuticorin, Chennai and Ennore Port Trusts, and the Dredging Corp. of India (DCI), were supposed to raise Rs. 971 crore in equity, the remaining Rs. 1,456.40 crore was to be a debt component according to the project's website.

After six weeks of lobbying, 10 banks, including Deutsche Bank and the Dublin-based Depfa Bank, agreed to extend credit. Because the Union government guaranteed the loans, banks did not have to perform a risk analysis, nor worry about capital adequacy.

While Axis was raising the debt component of the financing, Sethusamudram simultaneously floated tenders for the dredging work. The DCI was nominated to do a quarter of the work the rest of the dredging was to be done by third-party contractors, according to the project's economic feasibility study. Nearly 80% of the project outlay is estimated to be dredging, hence these tenders were the most important part of the process.

Bidders included Korea-based Hyundai Dredging International, Netherlands-based Van Oord International and Belgium-based JanBe Nul.

"But the lowest quote was about 80 or 90% higher than what was estimated," said Singh to Mint newspaper. "This represented the first setback for the project. From then on, the project has just unraveled", Singh said.

In 2006, as project costs escalated, DCI was nominated to do all the work. But it cannot do this work without help from other dredging companies : "it does not have the equipment needed," said an official at the DCI office in Rameshwaram to Ms. Narain. He requested anonymity, citing a gag order! But inexplicably, on the very next day, January 23, 2007, the Asian Age reported that the DCI dredger imported from Holland had broken into two and sunk into the sea when it began work on the Rama Setu. The DCI crane that went to pick up the dredger pieces also broke and sank. The Russian engineer consultant who went to inspect the mishap slipped and broke his leg. All these inexplicable coincidences has only fortified the divine mystique of Sri Rama and the faith in the Setu.

As of now, the expected shipping will not amortise the cost of SSCP (including maintenance, regular dredging costs, costs of pilots, tugs, support vessels, communication and radar infrastructure), leave alone earn profits. Who then will use the SSCP —even if we 'overlook' the LTTE Sea Tiger threat next door, the ever-present problem of cyclones (between 1891-2001, according to the Met Department, 64 cyclones crossed the TN coast, with 23 crossing the SSCP area) piracy, smuggling, marine pollution fights over fishing rights, gun and drug running mafia operations, tsunami and so on?

There is also the security angle to be considered. Once the SSCP becomes operational, policing it would require a major increase in the Indian Coast Guard, the Customs and Marine Police and in their assets in Rameshwaram and Tuticorin. Keeping in mind the increased proximity of Tuticorin to the Palk Bay due to the SSCP, the Indian Navy too may have to consider permanently basing some assets in Tuticorin for more intensive surveillance, and protection to future oil exploration rigs, and to insure a quick response to threats from the LTTE. It would require close co-ordination and timely intelligence sharing between all these agencies, and of course additional budget allocations.

Moreover, while the Project's economical viability is being viewed only from the shipping angle (i.e., about the cost of fuel, speed, safety, tonnage etc)., no one has given a good look at the figures both present and projected, re the actual demand at Tuticorin for freight movement, both breakbulk as well as bulk, for both chartered ships and container ships. We must study this aspect with respect to economical viability are the export and import from Tuticorin port: after all the SSCP is meant for serving mainly Tuticorin port (besides some of the minor ports in the future).

The main imports at Tuticorin are –

(a) *Copper* – Yearly, 5 lac tonnnes of sterlite copper are imported from Chile, Peru, Australia, South Africa, Indonesia, Mexico etc. Except for Australia, none of the above supplies originate from an area where the shipper would be interested in utilising the channel. In the case of Indonesia, supply originates in Padang in Sumatra and from there ships would prefer to call via Colombo. Also shipments come in lots of 45,000 mts and above, in handimax ships or panamax ships of 80,000 mts and above. Thus none of these would need to use the channel at all.

(b) *Sterlite* – This is the main import at Tuticorin.

(c) *Coal* – This is imported mainly by the Tuticorin thermal unit of the National Power Project. Yearly about 5 lacs tonnes is imported mainly from Indonesia and it comes in lots of 35,000 mts and above. Since it comes from Sumatra island mainly Padang and Palemeng, again shippers prefer to come via Colombo and they would not need to use the channel.

(d) *Rock phosphate* – Yearly 3 lacs tones comes from Jordan in the Middle East ;and of course there is no need to use the channel.

(e) *Urea* is imported from middle east ports like Saudia Arabia and other gulf countries, so again there is no need to use the channel

(f) *Petroleum coke* – This comes from South Africa and China. Russia also supplies some.

Exports out of Tuticorin port are:

(1) *Salt* – Yearly a maximum of three or four shiploads, in lots of a maximum of 3000 MTS, is shipped to east and west Malaysia. These would use the channel as their tonnage is smaller and their route is towards the direction of the channel.

(2) *Garnet sand* –Besides shipping this to China, South Korea, Taiwan and Malaysia, garnet sand is also sent to Dubai, Aden and Saudi Arabia, where it is used in sandblasting for oil pipes and in the abrasive industries. Yearly a further five shiploads each of a maximum of 5000 mts, would be shipped to South East Asia and a further five shiploads to the Gulf countries. Of these only the shipping to Korea, Taiwan and China would use the channel. This would amount to hardly 5 ships in a year, each of a maximum of 5000 to 6000 mts.

(3) *Sugar* – This is sent, mainly in unrefined sugar form as well as raw sugar, to European countries. A few shiploads are sent to Indonesia; but most of the sugar shipments go to Sri Lanka.

(4) *Maize* – This is sent mainly to Sri Lanka, as well as to Malaysian/Vietnam ports. Yearly five or six ships each of a maximum of 4000 to 5000 mts are sent to Malaysia and Vietnam from Tuticorin, and these could use the channel. Ships going to Srilanka would not use the channel.

It must be noted that sugar, maize and salt are seasonal commodities. Shipments are not round the year but only for a maximum of four to five months; hence total shipments of all the above, utilizing the channel, will be about 15 ships per year.

(5) *Container Shipments* – Presently, all container shipments from Tuticorin go to Colombo in feeder ships; and from Colombo they proceed further in mother ships of bigger tonnage. This is after combining all containers assembled at Colombo from ports like Chennai, Calcutta, Mumbai, Kandla, Cochin, Aden, Dubai, Mombasa, Dare s-Salem and other East African ports. None of the container ships would use the channel except container shipments of Colombo bound ships from Chennai and Calcutta ports; but no other container ships would so use, because most of the shipments of containers would go to Singapore for onward transshipments to other destination. Containers meant for Colombo only, could use the channel; but. the Sri Lanka market is very small. Since Paradip, Vizag, Kakinada do not have any container terminals, there is no container shipments activity from these ports to Colombo.

Because their decisions are based on commercial considerations, the perspective of ship owners is different from that of the Government:

(1) No ship owner ever calculates the savings on fuel etc. as he would leave this to the master of the ship and its chief officer; and their concern is mainly regarding the safety of the ship rather than the saving of a few thousand dollars. If they are not satisfied with the safety of the ship, they would simply drop out even if they could save one million dollars in going via the channel.

(2) The freight market is determined not by savings on fuel cost etc, but by demand and supply of market of cargos available in the region nearby.

Due to the Olympic games in 2009, there is a demand for steel products in construction industries in China; and hence China has started buying steel items and iron ore in a big way from India, pushing steel prices and iron ore prices by three times in just two years worldwide. This has resulted in many old ships of smaller sizes 3000/5000 DWTS and medium ships of 10,000/15,000/20,000 DWTS being sold to China. All such old and medium/small ships have been demolished and sold to Chinese steel units as steel scrap!

Moreover, the savings on crew wages and the larger freight earnings from bigger ships, have forced owners to choose bigger tonnage ships instead of smaller ships. Hence in the shipping market, one does not get smaller or medium ships anymore but only ships above 30,000 DWT and up to 85,000 mts. And now that the trend is advancing towards ships of 1,50,000 DWT tonnages, even the Suez canal and Panama canal (with depths of 14-18 meters in both canals) will be bypassed.

Interestingly, when AK Ventaka Subramanian IAS (Retd) filed a question with the TRTI/PIO seeking information on the benefits from the SSCP for the Tamil Nadu State owned Poompuhar Shipping Corporation Ltd, he received the astounding reply on 18.12.2007, 2½ years after the project was inaugurated b y the Prime Minister that: "This information is not available on the records of the Poompuhar Shipping Corporation Ltd" (See Annexure 18).

How then can the SSCP ever be considered viable? Obviously the Project has been promoted for the oblique motives of some political interests groups, without a proper economic auditor analysis. The *Times of India* (February 13, 2008) reported that the Union Shipping Minister Mr. T.R. Baalu made at least two trips at the tax payers expense to Egypt and Singapore costing Rs. 11 lakhs but chose not to take any official with him, nor file any report about the visist upon return. This is a breach of ethics and smells of a corrupt motive.

A future government must investigate this wellnigh criminal attempt to squander the tax payers' public funds, as well as the oblique and biased motives behind abandoning Alignment No. 4 in favour of the present Alignment No. 6 that cuts through the Rama Setu.

CHAPTER 5

National Security and other Concerns

Recently, (January 31, 2008), the Director General of Coast Guards, Vice Admiral Homi Contractor warned that the SSCP would increase the national security threats from terrorists, and principally from pirates, narcotics smugglers and especially the LTTE. He confirmed to media persons that he had conveyed this apprehension to the Government recently. Captain (Retd) H. Balakrishnan of the Indian Navy has presented a very good analysis in his study "The SSCP and Security", at a seminar of experts in Chennai on November 3, 2007. Based on this paper, I have summarized some of the main national security related threats that could result because of vessels navigating through the SSCP channel. These are:

(*a*) Maritime Terrorism of LTTE and Jihadis

(*b*) Piracy and Armed Robbery at sea

(*c*) Adverse Environmental Impact

(*d*) Erosion and Loss of Thorium Monazite Sands

A. MARITIME TERRORISM OF LTTE AND JIHADIS

Recent developments on the seas have made security analysts veer around increasingly to the view that the lines of demarcation between piracy and terrorism is fading. The LTTE has an impressive track record in this game. Some of the reported cases which relate to hijacking are of the vessels, IRISH MONA (Aug 1995), PRINCESS WAVE (Aug 1996), ATHENA (May 1997), MISEN (Jul 1997), MORONG BONG (Jul 1997), CORDIALITY (Sep 1997) and PRINCESS KASH (Aug 1998).

Piracy on the High Seas is becoming a key tactic of terrorist groups such as LTTE and Jihadis. Unlike the pirates of an earlier era, whose sole objective was quick commercial gain, many of today's pirates are "Maritime terrorists" with an "ideological bent and a broad political agenda". The nexus of Piracy and Terrorism is dangerous for the world energy markets, yet the SSCP has shown scant interest in this subject. Moreover, today, in the face of massive international efforts to freeze terrorist finances, terrorist groups have come to view piracy as a potentially rich source of funding. The appeal is particularly apparent in the Straits of Malacca. According to Indonesia's state intelligence agency, detained senior members of the Jemaah Islamiyah have admitted that the group has considered launching attacks on Malacca Straits shipping. Also, uniformed members of the Free Aceh Movement, an Indonesian separatist group, have been increasingly hijacking vessels and taking their crews as hostage. The protracted ransom negotiations yield considerable sums—the going rate is nearly $100,000 per ship. The ransom is later used to procure weapons for operations against the Indonesian Government. In some cases, the Free Aceh Movement has demanded the release of members detained by the Indonesian Government.

Geography forces world shipping to pass through strategic chokepoints, many of which are located in areas where terrorists with maritime capabilities operate. These channels are so narrow at certain points, that a single burning super tanker and its spreading oil slick could block the passage for other vessels. Were "terrorist – pirates" to hijack a large bulk carrier or tanker, sail it onto one of these choke points, and scuttle it to block the sea lane, the consequences for the world economy could be quite severe.

According to a PTI newsitem dated November 26, 2007, which cited a senior Naval officer, the LTTE (whose movement on the Tamil Nadu coast has been severely curtailed by the constant surveillance of the Indian Navy and Coastguard —and constant warnings from public figures such as Jayalalitha, N. Ram, Cho Ramaswamy and this author) has started shifting its operations to the Kerala coast. "The Indian Navy had increased vigil on the Tamil Nadu coast, making it virtually impenetrable", said Flag officer Commanding-in-Chief Southern Naval Command, Vice Admiral Sunil K Damle.

Attempts are therefore being made by the LTTE, to begin using the Kerala coast for smuggling arms, ammunition narcotics and drugs. Consequently too, efforts are being made by Jihadi terrorist organizations with an ISI connection, to use Malabar as a landing point for RDX explosive. This means that once the Rama Setu is breached and the channel is created, the channel would vastly facilitate the transit of LTTE ships from Jaffna (which is north of the Rama Setu), to Trivandrum and Kochi (both south of the Setu). Given the DMK's record of aiding and abetting LTTE activities in the recent past, the insistence by its Party's Ministers on implementing the SSCP acquires a sinister dimension of national security risk.

In his paper, "Maritime Terrorism: An Indian Perspective", delivered by security analyst, Mr. B. Raman at an International Conference held at Singapore in 2004, the author stated:

> "Apprehensions of major acts of maritime terrorism by terrorist organizations, which are members of Osama bin Laden's "International Islamic Front – (IIF)", continue to be high, but there are no clear indicators so far of their having already acquired the necessary capability for such acts. However, their nexus with trans-national mafia groups, like the one headed by Pakistan based Dawood Ibrahim, has placed at their disposal maritime facilities which could be used and are being used for the clandestine movement of trained men and material required for land based terrorist operations in other countries".

In this context, it is pertinent to mention here that the explosives for the 1993 Mumbai blasts, imported through this very Saine Dawood Ibrahim, came by sea.

In an interview to the British shipping bulletin, "Lloyds List" (Aug 6, 2004) the British First Sealord, Admiral Sir Alan West was

quoted as stating that Al Qaeda and other terrorist groups had
realized the importance of global maritime trade and could launch
attacks against merchant vessels. Admiral Sir Alan West then stated:

> "We have got an underlying level of intelligence which shows
> there is a threat. What we've noticed is that Al Qaeda and other
> organizations have an awareness about maritime trade. They've
> realized how important it is for world trade in general, and they
> understand the significance. Sea borne terrorism could potentially
> cripple global trade and have grave knock-on effects on developed
> economies. We've seen other plans from intelligence of attacks on
> merchant shipping. I can't give you clear detail on any of that,
> clearly, but we are aware that they have plans. Ship owners realize
> that".

It may be argued that in comparison to acts of terrorism in the skies
and on land, such acts either in inland waters or on the high seas have
been few, and could be overlooked. Such a view is premature
because of two factors, namely:-

(1) Except in the case of suicide terrorist acts, where escape is not
     a factor, getting away after an act of maritime terrorism on the
     high seas is not an easy task;

(2) Terrorists want a "stage" to enact their drama in order to derive
     the maximum publicity and have a psychological intimidatory
     impact on the minds of their perceived State adversaries as also
     its citizens.

A discernable trend at present, which is extremely disturbing, is the
spread of increasingly sophisticated conventional weapons to non-
state actors, including long range anti-ship missiles, unmanned aerial
vehicles and close range armor piercing missiles and rocket propelled
grenades. All these varieties of munitions are capable of inflicting
serious damage to ships, both large and small. The trade in small
arms and light infantry weapons is already extensive in the conflict

prone parts of the globe and the demand for more advanced equipment is strong.

The problem is global in scope. There are around 100 countries that make weapons and ammunition, and sell these products (over $1 trillion (in 2006)).

The list of foiled, failed and successful attempts in maritime related terrorism over the past decade is significant. Terrorists see the potential of using the maritime trading system, and its land links in the container supply chain, to conceal weapons or agents for attack purposes. Three recent examples should suffice to illustrate the maritime terrorist threat:

(a) *Attack on the U.S.S. Cole*: In October 2000, Al Qaeda operatives in Yemen, packed a small boat with explosives and rammed the same into the side of the U.S. Navy destroyer, U.S.S. Cole, while the ship was berthed in harbor. The blast left a gaping hole in the side of the destroyer and the cost of repairs amounted to $250 million. The blast killed 17 U.S. Naval sailors and wounded another 40 seamen.

(b) *Missile Attack on Israeli Naval Ships*: On 14 July 2006, two days after hostilities between Israel and the Hezbollah commenced, the latter fired two C-802 radar guided anti-ship cruise missiles from the seashore in Lebanon. The targets were two Israeli naval corvettes that were patrolling off the Lebanese coast. One missile seriously damaged one of the corvettes, killing four Israeli seamen. The second missile narrowly missed the other corvette. Instead it hit a Cambodian registered merchant vessel, which sank immediately taking with it all the eleven seaman on board.

(c) *Attack on the French VLCC Limburg*: In Oct 2002, a boat packed with explosives, rammed into the side of the French VLCC Limburg, of Yemen, and seriously damaged the vessel. The tanker had a capacity of 300,000 tons. Fortunately, at the time of the incident, it was loaded with only 55,000 tons of crude oil. This attack disrupted Yemen's oil trade for a short period.

For India, the terrorist organization to be concerned about, is of course the LTTE with its "Sea Tigers" naval arm (which has developed rapidly and now has a capability for acts of maritime terrorism). It has a fleet of at least two or three merchant vessels, playing under flags of convenience. Normally these transport legitimate cargo; but when required to do so, they are also used for clandestinely transporting military hardware procured by the LTTE in countries like Pakistan Thailand, Ukraine, and earlier from Iraq and Cambodia.

Two significant aspects of the LTTE's gun-running capability by sea, have to be noted. Firstly, the LTTE's willingness to place its capability, on contract, at the disposal of other terrorist organizations. There is at least one reported instance in 1995, of the LTTE helping either the Abu Sayyaf or the Moro Islamic Liberation Front(both based in the Philippines), by carrying a consignment of arms and ammunition donated by Harkat-ul-Mujahideen (HUM), from Pakistan to Southern Philippines. Secondly, it uses merchant vessels not belonging to it, for the purpose of gun running. In 1993, a foreign merchant vessel carrying AK 47s, from a Russian company, arrived in Cochin. The consignee, was ostensibly our Defence Ministry! But this was on false identity papers. Indian intelligence strongly suspect the LTTE hand in this botched attempt at gun running.

At present the Sea Tigers of the LTTE have established control over most of the northern Sri Lanka coastal region and the seas contiguous to this coast. They have displayed considerable ingenuity and daring in sea borne insurgency. They have carried out numerous daring attacks on Sri Lankan naval ships, and have not hesitated in undertaking suicide missions. Their daring attack on the naval installations on Delft Island, this summer, is a case in point. Thus the Alignment No. 6 of the SSCP is verily a "next-door-neighbour" of the Sea Tigers lair.

A new addition to the LTTE's fighting capability is its "Air Arm". They have to date carried out four daring night attacks on Sri Lankan military assets. A new factor seen in the last attack was their ability to co-ordinate the land and air attacks. The SSCP falls well within the radius of operation of the 'ZLIN-Z242L" the Czech aircraft which the LTTE operates..... Who provided the equipment and training for flying missions of this aircraft? Probably some rogue state of Asia.

Media reports of April 28, 2007 in Chennai, attributed the killings of Tamil fishermen at sea to the LTTE Sea Tigers. The grounds for killing the fishermen, attributed to LTTE sources, was that they were "spying" on the LTTE's activities at sea. If that be the case, the possibility of the LTTE advancing a similar argument for attacking ships navigating through the channel cannot be ruled out. The consequences of a ship sinking/running aground in the channel could have a disastrous impact on the very viability of the Project itself. It would have a psychological impact, as brought out earlier, on the shipping industry which may then tend to bypass the channel.

The prevailing depths in the channel make it an ideal area for the use of sea mines. The acquisition of sophisticated conventional arms by various terrorist organisations, has already been highlighted. A rudimentary sea mine is far cheaper than any of the sophisticated missiles. And yet, such a mine can block the channel from being used for protracted durations as Mine Countermeasures (MCM) is a slow, tedious and time consuming form of naval warfare. This threat needs to be seriously kept in mind while formulating security policies for the channel. It is hoped that the lessons learnt from MCM operations in the Straits of Hormuz during and after Operation Desert Storm is not lost on our policy planners.

B. PIRACY AND ARMED ROBBERY BY CRIMINALS

The internationally accepted "definition" of piracy is contained in
Article 101 of the 1982 U.N. Convention on the Law of the Seas
(UNCLOS):

"Piracy consists of any of the following acts:

(1) Any illegal acts of violence or detention, or any act of
    depradation, committed for private ends by the crew or the
    passengers of a private ship or a private aircraft, and directed:

    (*i*) On the High Seas, against another ship or aircraft or
         against persons or property on board such ship or aircraft;

    (*ii*) Against a ship, aircraft, persons or property in a place
          outside the jurisdiction of any state;

(2) Any act of voluntary participation in the operation of a ship
    or of an aircraft with knowledge of facts making it a pirate ship
    or aircraft;

(3) Any act inciting or of intentionally facilitating an act described
    in (a) or (b)."

Acts of piracy and armed robbery against ships are of tremendous
concern to shipping in general. The fight to suppress these acts is
linked to the Convention for Suppression of Unlawful Acts against
the Safety of Maritime Navigation, and to Improve Security
Measures on Board Ships and in Port Facilities- 1988, adopted in
Dec. 2002.

According to reports compiled by the IMO, between 1984 and
the end of 1999, there had been 1587 attacks by pirates on ships
around the world. In some areas, these attacks involved a disturbing
increase in violence. Contrary to the stereotype, today's pirates are
often trained fighters aboard speedboats, equipped with satellite
phones and Global Positioning System (GPS) and armed with
automatic weapons.

The International Maritime Bureau Piracy Reporting Centre
(IMB), was set up in Oct. 1992 and located at Kuala Lumpur,

Malaysia. Financed by voluntary contributions from shipping and insurance companies, its services are free of charge to all vessels irrespective of ownership and flag. Its specific tasks are:

(*i*) To report all piracy incidents and armed robbery at sea to concerned law enforcement agencies;

(*ii*) To locate vessels that have been seized by pirates and recover stolen cargoes;

(*iii*) To help bring the pirates to justice;

(*iv*) To assist owners and crews of ships that have been attacked;

(*v*) To collate information on piracy around the world.

Based on data from this Centre, Captain Balakrishnan has compiled the following figures;

Table 7
Consequences of Piracy on High Seas

Number of Acts of Piracy		*Lives Lost*	*Wounded*	*Missing*	*Ships hijacked*	*Missing*	*Lost*
2000	470	70	130	40	2	2	Nil
2001	370	20	40	10	2	3	1
2002	390	10	50	10	12	8	1
2003	430	15	40	10	11	11	2
2004	310	30	85	40	9	Nil	3
2005	260	Nil	150	15	16	Nil	Nil

In the Arabian Sea, in November 1999, Indian Maritime Forces had rescued the "hijacked" M.V. ALONDRA RAINBOW, a 7000 Ton Panama registered vessel, belonging to Japanese owners. The vessel was on passage from Kuala Tanjung in Indonesia to Milke in Japan. The IMB Piracy Reporting Centre had put out a worldwide broad cast of the incident. According to the IMB Centre, the crew of the vessel had been located safe in Thailand and the vessel was expected to turn up at any Indian port to discharge her cargo. After a drama on the high seas, the hijacked vessel was captured and the pirates brought to justice. However, on an appeal in the Bombay High Court, some years later, the pirates were set free!

Implications under International Law of the Sea, of damaging the Rama Setu

In Alignment No. 6, the arbitrary unthinking choice of the medial line as the passage channel, raises serious concerns of national sovereignty and security, : it may actually result in the creation of an international boundary in what have always (or at least since 1974) been considered to be Historic (Internal) Waters of India and Sri Lanka. The medial line was only an administrative boundary to delimit ownership of chank and pearl fishery areas between India and Sri Lanka and it must not be allowed to be converted into a international waters boundary.

As stated earlier, the new channel alignment now being implemented, was never considered by any of the previous committees since 1860 (when Commander Taylor proposed a canal). Therefore, as evidenced by the U.S. Navy Operational Directive of 23 June 2005, this channel alignment will only satisfy the US interests which refuse to recognize India's claim and Sri Lanka's claim to the Gulf of Mannar and Palk Straits and Palk Bay as Historic (Internal) Waters. In fact, during 1993, 1994 and 1999 the U.S. had sought to impose its naval might by sending battleships there. The U.S. Directive states:

"This claim (of historic waters) is not recognized by the United States. U.S. conducted operational assertions in 1993 and 1994, to Gulf of Mannar claim in 1999." This stance of USA is in direct contravention of:

- United Nations Conference on the Law of the Sea (1958), Convention of the Territorial Sea and Contiguous Zone recognizes Historic Waters;
- The Agreement between Sri Lanka and India on the Maritime Boundary between the Two Countries in the Gulf of Mannar and the Bay of Bengal and Related Matters dated 23 March 1976.

Therefore, by choosing a Setu Samudram Channel alignment running very close to international waters and involving damage to the Rama Setu, India is going back on its earlier claims of these waters being historic waters.

By keeping the alignment close to the 'international' waters the Coast Guard will be handicapped in protecting the channel from the Sri Lanka side— since Coast Guard vessels will have to constantly get into international waters.

It will therefore make eminent sense in terms of the juridical regime of historic and internal waters to choose an alignment close to Pamban Island without damaging the Rama Setu. The relevant extracts from UN documents are given below:

The first United Nations Conference on the Law of the Sea (1958) adopted (in Paragraph 6 of Article 7 of the Convention of the Territorial Sea and Contiguous Zone), a provision to the effect that its rules on bays "shall not apply to so-called 'historic' bays" [United Nations, Treaty Series, vol.516, p.210].

The Conference also adopted on 27 April 1958 a resolution requesting the General Assembly to arrange for the study of the juridical regime of historic waters, including historic bays. The General Assembly thereafter adopted resolution 1453 (XIV) of 7 December 1959 which requested the International Law Commission, "as soon as it considers it advisable, to undertake the study of the question of the juridical regime of historic waters, including historic bays, and to make such recommendations regarding the matter as the Commission deems appropriate"

The Commission, at its twelfth session (1960) requested the Secretariat to undertake a study of the topic, and deferred further consideration to a future session. A study prepared by the Secretariat *was* published m 1962. Also in 1962, the Commission, at its fourteenth session, decided to include the topic in its programme, but without setting any date for the start of its consideration. At its nineteenth session (1967), the Commission examined the advisability of proceeding actively with the study of this topic. The Commission's report summarised the views expressed, as follows:

> "Most members doubted whether the time had yet come to proceed actively with either of these topics."

The Agreement between Sri Lanka and India on the Maritime Boundary between the two Countries in the Gulf of Mannar and the Bay of Bengal and Related Matters, 23 March 1976 states:

> "The Government of the Republic of Sri Lanka and the Government of the Republic of India, recalling that the boundary in the Palk Strait has been settled by the Agreement between the Republic of Sri Lanka and the Republic of India on the Boundary in Historic Waters between the Two Countries and Related Matters, signed on 26/28 June, 1974; and desiring to extend that boundary by determining the maritime boundary between the two countries in the Gulf of Mannar and the Bay of Bengal, have agreed as follows:

...Article 5

> (1) Each Party shall have sovereignty over the historic waters and territorial sea, as well as over the islands, falling on its side of the aforesaid boundary.
> (2) Each Party shall have sovereign rights and exclusive jurisdiction over the continental shelf and the exclusive economic zone as well as over their resources, whether living or non-living, falling on its side of the aforesaid boundary.
> (3) Each Party shall respect rights of navigation through its territorial sea and exclusive economic zone in accordance with its laws and regulations and the rules of international law."

In summary, the concept of "historic waters" has its root in the historic fact that States through the ages claimed and maintained sovereignty over maritime areas which they considered vital to them without paying much attention to divergent and changing opinions about what general international law might prescribe with respect to the delimitation of the territorial sea. It was felt that States could not be expected to accept rules which would deprive them of considerable maritime areas over which they had hitherto had sovereignty. [http:// untreaty.un.org/ilc/documentation/english/a cn4 143. pdf]

EROSION AND LOSS OF THORIUM MONAZITE SANDS

Importance of thorium for nuclear program:

According to the Bhabha Atomic Energy Commission (BARC) website. India has known Thorium deposits of 3,60,000 tonnes approximately. This currently known Indian thorium reserve amount to 358,000 GWe-yr of electrical energy and hence can easily meet the energy requirements of the nation during the next century and beyond. [http://www.barc.ernet.in/webpages/about/anu1.htm].

India's vast thorium deposits make feasible for us the indigenous design and operation of U-33 fuelled breeder reactors.

These U-233/Th-232 based breeder reactors are presently under development, and would serve as the mainstay of the final Thorium utilization stage of the Indian nuclear programme, and make India completely self-reliant.

Interestingly, the Rama Setu has been instrumental in the accumulation of placer deposits of Thorium:it acts acting like a sieve against the ocean currents and ocean counter currents of the Gulf of Mannar. The impact of cutting a hole through Rama Setu on this ongoing accumulation of the world's largest reserves of Thorium has to be studied by a multi disciplinary team of experts because it could cause a major erosion of deposition of Thorium on the South Indian coastline. Another tsunami of the type which struck the coastline on Dec 26, 2004 will draw the energy of the tsunami through this channel passage and devastate the Thorium accumulations and also make it virtually impossible to retrieve the precious mineral, so critical for the nation's nuclear program, Thorium reserves in Manavalakurichi (Tamilnadu), Aluva and Chavara (Kerala) have the potential to serve the electricity generation needs of the nation for the next 400 years.

Respecting the agreement on Historic Waters signed between Smt. Indira Gandhi and Smt. Sirimavo Bandaranaike in June 1974, any idea of cutting a channel passage through Rama Setu close to the medial line should therefore be abandoned.

Thus, by choosing a channel passage running close to the medial line, a new phenomenon is sought to be created: an international waters boundary between India and Srilanka. A medial line is only relevant for recognizing the ownership of ocean properties of shanka (chank) and pearl fisheries. Traditionally, fishermen and pearl-divers had the freedom to move across the medial line treating the waters as historic, internal waters. US Navy Operational Directive of 23 June 2005 treating these as international waters is therefore a serious threat to nation's sovereignty and integrity.

CHAPTER 6

The Environmental Implications of SSCP

1. SUMMARY /OVERVIEW OF THE SHORTCOMINGS OF THE NEERI REPORT

As will be developed hereinbelow in paras 4(a) to 4 (q), the Project and the channel will have an enormous adverse, irreversible impact on the environment, most of which impact has not been addressed by the NEERI Report. Let alone the huge dramatic impacts, the Report is yet to deal with even lesser side-effects like the sedimentation problem, silting possibilities and underwater ocean currents, which may result when the SSCP channel is constructed.

Even the data used (meagre and unsatisfactory as it is) is defective and outdated : according to Sudharshan Rodriguez, a Chennai-based conservation analyst, the Environment Impact Assessment (EIA) Report furnished by NEERI, has used secondary data which was outdated even in 1976. Hence, he has questioned how the Project, construction on which commenced only in 2005 and which will pass through a biological hot spot with so many likely impacts, could be assessed on the basis of such outdated 1976 secondary data.

This shoddy work by the NEERI may be understandable because on April 8, 1999, the Environment Ministry addressed a letter to the Gopalan Steering Group stating that "this Ministry is of the strong opinion that from the environmental angle, this Project should not be taken up at all. "[see Annexure 5]. Ossie Fernandez, the Convenor, Indian Coastal Action Network, has alleged that the

NEERI EIA Report is also a re-hash of the preliminary report and that, many activists and professionals are querying the data sources, including the bio diversity readings.

In early April 2007, the Sri Lanka government handed to India, the Report of a 34 member Advisory Group on the implications of the SSCP. The concern of Sri Lanka is that the initial dredging, the continuous maintenance dredging, and the presence of shipping in the channel, could have negative impact on Sri Lanka's maritime and environment resources. The Sri Lankan concern recently expressed to the Government of India, is that the Indian studies have not taken into account a single environment impact on the Sri Lankan side of the international boundary.

The Sri Lankan Advisory Group is of the view that, despite the channel being located only one mile inside the Indian side of the maritime boundary, the impact is unlikely to remain only on the Indian side; and Sri Lanka's concerns have become even more significant, in the light of insufficient attention paid to minimise the environmental aspects on the Sri Lankan side of the boundary. The Advisory Group has also itemized the reasons why the Environmental Impact Assessment (EIA) carried out by India is inadequate.

Interalia, in defence of the Sri Lankan Advisory Group Report, it must be pointed out that the NEERI Report itself being flawed, this alone was sufficient legal justification to put the entire NEERI Report into scientific question. The concerns that Sri Lanka has expressed on protecting endangered species, fisheries resources, the coastal and maritime eco diversity system, integrity of the eco system in the seas around the island and immediate and long-term ecological stability, are therefore legitimate.

It is also admitted by the Minister of Culture, Government of India that no maritime archaeology study has been conducted on this site. Thirteen thousand years ago, the area around the Kalpitiya lagoon, up to Mannar, was forested. Even today, stumps of old trees are found underwater. Yet no studies have been conducted.

2. VALIDITY OF THE ENVIRONMENTAL CLEARANCE

In the first place, what is the validity of the environmental clearances given by the Government of India to the SSCP?

Environmental clearance for the Sethusamudram Shipping Canal Project was obtained under Environmental Impact Assessment Notification (1994) 16011//6/99-1A-III dated 31.03.2005 subject to certain conditions. (see Annexure 6) On 27th January, 1994, the Government of India had issued a general Notification issued under Rule 5(3)(A) of the Environment (Protection) Rules, 1986. Thereunder, within 60 days from the date of the Notification, there must be invited from the public, objections in respect of certain activities. This applies to any new project in any part of India. Also no new project is to be undertaken in any part of India, unless the same has been accorded Environment Clearance by the Central Government in accordance with the procedure laid down in the said Notification. This notification was amended on 10.04.1997.

There is no question that the Sethusamudram Shipping Canal Project, a mega project involving close to Rs. 2000 crores, comprehending interalia the disturbance of the delicate marine ecosystems of the Gulf of Mannar Biosphere Reserve, and involving the livlihood of lakhs of persons, requires such Objection-hearings and Clearance. Since the marine organisms of the Gulf of Mannar are protected by the Wildlife Protection Act of India (1982), the Project required Clearance from the Ministry of Environment and Forests. Certainly this Project is bound to have a lasting impact on the biodiversity in the area and it could also change the life style of the traditional fishermen and lead to their impoverishment. Any rehabilitation program for them, will help only on a short-term basis. But for their long term survival, a long-term program to protect the Biosphere is needed.

A Rapid Environmental Impact Assessment (REIA) was done by the National Environmental Engineering Research Institute, Nagpur. Public hearings were held in September 2004 and November 2004 on the issue of whether to accord approval to the Project. These hearings, which are actually an attempt to involve the public in environmental decision-making consistent with India's acceptance of the Rio Declaration and its follow up, were marked by almost unanimous opposition to the Project from the fishing community and from environmentalists. Environmentalists and activists from local communities pointed out how issues like tsunamis and cyclones were ignored in the study. This was to prove prophetic in the light of the tsunami experienced off the Indian coast (including the proposed Project site) on December 26, 2004.

After the December 2004 tsunami, public hearings were resumed in February 2005—this, though people from the fishing communities had been affected by the tsunami and were in relief camps and thus were unable to attend the hearings. However the hearings went ahead; and then, by its Clearance dated 31/03/05, the Ministry granted the go-ahead for the Project.

In May 2004, NEERI reported its REI Assessment to the Nodal Agency namely Tuticorin Port Trust. And by July 2004, the Detailed Project Report (DPR) and the Techno Economic Feasibility Report (TEFR) were submitted by Larsen and Toubro of India and Ramboll of Denmark who are the contractors for the SSCP.

The aspects with which these environment protections are concerned are set out hereinbelow.

3. VITIATED PUBLIC HEARINGS AND DEFECTIVE AND INCOMPLETE APPROVALS

(a) The public hearings relating to the Project proposal, were conducted by panels which were not duly constituted panels. Public hearings were mere formalities and not substantive compliance and did not achieve the purpose for which they were visualized. It was only a procedural compliance but not substantive compliance. Even the procedural compliance was defective as panelists hearing the public were not duly constituted in accordance with notification. Further, the public hearings were without a comprehensive Environment Impact Assessment.

(b) Furthermore the proceedings granting environmental clearance were vitiated, the Clearance being issued without application of mind to relevant facts and details and without considering the inadequacy of the Rapid Environment Impact Assessment (REIA) report done by the National Environment Engineering Research Institute (NEERI).

The final Environmental Impact Assessment (EIA) has still not been made. Such EIA must be based on data; and since even according to NEERI a complete EIA "will have to be prepared *later* based on the data collection for the region", obviously such data has not yet been obtained and colated. The relevant part of the Report is extracted below:

".... This Rapid environmental impact assessment study report is to be prepared incorporating available baseline data for the region, environmental impact statement based on the identification, prediction and evaluation of impacts, ranking of environmentally viable alternatives and environmental management plan for the acceptable route. The comprehensive Rapid EIA report will be prepared *later* based on the primary data collection for the Region..." (Page 1.15)

This has not yet been done!

Therefore, it is submitted, a major project of such a nature has actually been cleared on the basis of only an REIA Report, despite that the agency which has made the REIA Report, clearly states the need for a comprehensive EIA Report which has not yet been made. It is thus admitted that the Report is not based on the primary data which has yet to be collected, more so after the tsunami.

(c) Even according to the said REIA Report, under paragraph 1.7 approval has to be obtained from the following ten agencies/ authorities.

1. Tamil Nadu State Pollution Control Board
2. Tamil Nadu State Forest & Environment Department
3. Tamil Nadu Maritime Board
4. State Wildlife Warden
5. Chief Conservator of Forests
6. Ministry of Environment & Forests
7. Ministry of Defence / Indian Navy
8. Archeological Department
9. Ministry of External Affairs
10. Sri Lankan Government

But in this vital matter, even without waiting for such approvals a political decision was made for the clearance of the project.

The matter goes deeper: at the time the Project was operationalised, the then Government of Tamil Nadu, took the stand that the procedure adopted for the impugned clearance was not proper, and that environmental and sociological factors had been ignored. Certainly, the subject matter of the   Project required State Government assent. Legislation relating to Maritime Shipping and Navigation comes under Entry 25 of List I (the Union List); but Entry 32 of List III (the Concurrent List) deals with "Shipping and navigation on inland water ways as regard mechanically propelled vessels and the rule of the road on such water ways and the carriage of passengers and goods of inland water ways subject to provisions of List I with respect to national waterways"; and Entry17-B of List III (the Concurrent List) deals with " Protection of wild animals and birds"; and List II(the State List) comprehends   two relevant Entries— "Fisheries" (Entry 21 of List II) and "Works, Lands, and Buildings vested in or in the possession of the State "(Entry 35 of List II).

Reading all these Entries together,it is submitted, that when a proposed activity like the Project also touches upon or enters an area on which the State Government has its powers, it is not in the spirit of the quasi federal nature of the Constitution of India to implement the Project without the specific consent of the State Government. Such consent had not been obtained at the time the Project was put into operation. Indeed it had specifically been denied, in that the specific stand of the State Government (as seen from the statement of the then Chief Minister, as reported in the press) as well as that of the Expert Committee appointed by the Tamil Nadu Pollution Control Board, was that NEERI's REIA was inadequate. It is submitted that on this ground also the impugned proceedings are liable to be quashed.

On the other hand, from day one, Mr. T.R. Baalu, the Minister for Shipping, Road Transport and Highways has been showing undue haste in pushing the Project; and even prior to consideration by the Government of India, the Minister for Environment gave his personal Clearance for the Project. The Minister has been making statements in public, that there would be no adverse environmental impact. The Minister has personally cleared the Project without following the statutory procedure and thereby has adversely affected an objective and rational evaluation of the environmental impact of the Project and the damage the same would cause.

4. DEFICIENCIES IN DATA COLLECTED AND REDUCED AMBIT OF PRE-PROJECT STUDIES

(*a*) A study of the EIA done by the NEERI, would show that it is confined to the impact of the activity on only the *actual area* covered by the proposed channel and not the impact on the surrounding areas of the channel. This is a very serious omission and a gaping hole in the EIA Report. The study requires not only the study of impact on the actual area in which the channel is to be dredged, but also the surrounding area.

The EIA Report ought to have considered the following aspects:

1. What would happen in the area that is to be dredged to create the channel.

2. The impact of the dredged sand on the location where it will be dumped?

3. Primary data collected and evaluated for the purpose of knowing the tide currents during different seasons and its impact on the coral reefs, mangrove and other flora/fauna by the dredged sand while the same is being dredged and also when it is dumped.

4. Impact of possible cyclones and tsunamis:the project area is known for frequent cyclones and tsunamis.

5. The impact of sedimentation on the coral reefs and other environmentally sensitive areas rich in bio diversity.

(b) As can be seen from other parts of the world, dredging of the ocean floor can have a lasting impact on the environment. The proposed area is world renowned for its rich biodiversity ;yet the Report claims that it is "only a sandy area". No doubt, this was done to emphasise that the Project would disturb only sand, which could be moved by simple dredging.

The Gulf of Mannar region has fast moving currents that can fill up the dredged passage with sediments, which will involve secondary dredging. Thus a lot of dredging effort could go waste.

The dredged material to be dumped in mid sea, could be diluted in no time and could be deposited as silt in the Gulf of Mannar. There will be an abrupt stop in fish catch since corals give shelter to marine organisms. There could also be deposition on the beach, covering ecosystems close to the shore like corals and mangrove vegetation. The coral reefs are sensitive ecosystems and siltation from dredging activities, deposited on the corals, could damage the coral reefs of the whole area, which could spell disaster to biodiversity in the region

Again it is questionable whether dredging in such a small area could facilitate the passage of ships. According to the impugned proceedings, the dredged material of 82.5 million cubic meters of capital dredging, is to be disposed of in the sea at a distance of 25 to 30 kilometers from the Rama Setu, in an area of 5km x 5km at geographical co-ordinates, 8.55 51.15"N and 79 26´54.81'E, and 10 13'14.05" N and 80 13'11.56"E. This identified site was never made the subject matter of the public hearing process. There was no disclosure of this location of the dumping site, and it was not the subject of analysis in the REIA Report.

Dredging will also reduce the photosynthetic rate, resulting in the collapse of the fishing industry. As already stated, the newspaper *Business Line* (October 16, 2007) reported the assertion of the International Shipping Association that once the SSCP is implemented and operationalised, fishing by trawlers and other means will have to be banned to enable ships to ply through the channel.

The Project visualized that the dredged material will also be disposed off in the land area that stretches between Kothandaswamy Temple and Dhanushkodi which is a wetland acting as a feeding ground for thousands of migratory birds during the winter season. Thus such feeding grounds will be disrupted.

The dredging proposed could also involve blasting, if the hard strata under the soft sediments were found to be hard rock.

To summarise therefore, on the aspect of dredging and its effects, the Government of India had almost no material to base its decision for clearance; and the decision to go ahead with the channel flies in the face of the aforesaid valid considerations.

(c) The problem of sedimentation has not been addressed at all. There is a crying need to thoroughly document the already available studies on sedimentation in Palk Bay; to take up further studies that will shed light on the pattern of sediment movement during normal times and during the periods of tropical cyclones and tsunamis; and to analyse the data acquired by such study.

In particular, there is a need to study the question as to how the Project will affect the situation at Palk Bay and thus how it will affect the coastlines of the two countries. Palk Bay is one of the five major permanent sediment sinks of India. This sediment load is said to cause a sea depth reduction of 1 cm/year. Rivers draining into the Palk Bay from the Sri Lankan and Indian coasts and the sea contribute sediments. The longshore currents from the Bay of Bengal in the north and the Gulf of Mannar in the south transport these sediments into Palk Bay. Although it has calculated the net annual sediment transport by long shore current and tides in the Rama Setu area, the REIA has not yet calculated. the sediment contribution from the rivers. Hence, 99.39% of the total sedimentation volume has not yet been accounted for.

During the construction phase of this project a large quantity of sediments will be dredged in the Palk Bay and Palk Strait regions. The study on tides and currents carried out by NEERI, indicates that there is a significant flow of materials into the Gulf of Mannar from the Palk Bay during the South West Monsoon season. The large amount of sediments dredged during the construction will be transported from Palk Bay to the Gulf of Mannar, through the Rama Setu and Pamban Pass; and large amounts of sediments dredged from Palk Bay during dredging will be deposited on the coral reefs of the Gulf, which would put them in peril. Entry of sediment laden water, from Palk Bay to the Gulf of Mannar through Rama Setu and Pamban Pass, will also affect the productivity of the sea grass beds located in the northern region of the Gulf of Mannar Biosphere Reserve. These sea grass beds are feeding grounds of the dugong and any damage to these beds would significantly affect the survival of the dugong.

(d) Furthermore, the environmental impact assessment study is vague on the impact of the massive dumping that would be involved with SSCP. The total quantity of dredged spoil that would come from capital dredging is expected to be 81.5 to 88.5 x 10^6 m^3. The quantum of dredged spoil that would come from maintenance dredging is calculated to be 0.1 x 10^6 m^3/year. A specific dumping site has been identified only for from 8.5 to 9.5% of this total dredged spoil and the Project has not earmarked the exact locations of dumping sites for about 90.5 to 91.5% of the dredged material. Furthermore the nature of the dredged spoil is currently known only for about 38.5 to 40.5% of the total dredged spoil.

Furthermore, there would be increased turbidity, which has never been studied by NEERI.

(e) The composition of the subsurface has been studied only for a 20 km stretch in the Rama Setu area. It has not been studied for the 54.2 km Palk Strait portion of the channel. If the subsurface turns out to be rocky, then blasting will have to be used in the construction of the channel; this is bound to increase manifold the cost of the channel, and also it is bound to cause unacceptedly high damage to the rich oceanographic environment around. There is a need to study the impact of such blasting on the ecology of the area and on the livelihood of the people living around it both in India and Sri Lanka The EIA has not even considered the possibility of needing to fall back on blasting.

The experience of last year's "dredging" in the area of the Rama Setu, has made it abundantly clear that there will have to be major blasting to enable the channel to be built in the Rama Setu area. The consequences of such blasting, in terms of ecological damage to a fragile unique biosphere, and the wound to the religious and cultural sentiments of all India, are so horrendous that on this ground alone, the Project must be scrapped.

(f) Besides dredging which results in turbidity, another source of pollution is from oil spills from the ships passing through the canal. Major oil spills from cargo spills are frequent events that have serious consequences on the environment. On the global scale, about 1% of all cargo vessels are involved in accidents resulting in oil spills. It may be mentioned that the traffic potential in the canal is estimated to be 11,000 ships per year which means that every three days there will be an accidental spill. It is worth mentioning that the sea bed surrounding the proposed route of the canal through the Rama Setu is shallow no more than 4m deep. Thus even a small deviation from the planned route would be catastrophic.

Transport of oil and fuel, usage of machineries, cleaning of ships will also cause further pollution.

(g) Most important of all, the REIA has not paid any serious attention to the meteorological factors. The east coast of India is subject to frequent cyclonic storms. These can disturb the sedimentation dynamics of the region and thus the quantity of dredging to be undertaken. Similarly, cyclones can rework the dumped material.. Added to that is the realization that the east coast is vulnerable to disasters like tsunamis. NEERI has not even studied the possibility of occurrence of a tsunami in the flow of water through the deep water channel linking the Indian Ocean and the Bay of Bengal.

In this context, one must recall the tsunami which occurred in December 2004. The epicenter of the earthquake, which triggered the tsunami, was located south west of Sumatra at the interface of the Indian and the Burmese plates. Due to the presence of the lithosphere boundary around the Simeuleus Islands which continues up to the Nicobar Islands, the earthquake rupture initiated west of this boundary did not cross to the east, but got propagated northwards to the Andaman and Nicobar Islands. The tsunami caused destruction in 12 countries, from Indonesia to Somalia. It killed 1,76,260 people. In addition, 49, 682 were reported missing. Indonesia suffered the maximum damage as the epicenter of the earthquake which initiated the tsunami was located there. It affected the Andaman and Nicobar Islands, Sri Lanka, the Tamil Nadu coast and, to a lesser extent, the Kerala coast. Further, it affected the southern part of the eastern continental shelf of India, from Karaikal in the south to Vishakapatnam in the north.

In particular, the Nagapattinam - Cuddalore portion was among the worst affected.. The reasons for the high sea surge in this area, were the bathymetry of the shelf and the concave configuration of the coastline It has been noted that the Palk Bay received tsunami waves of higher energy and that these could not directly pass on to the Gulf of Mannar due to the presence of the Rama Setu. The waves taking a higher arc, circumventing Sri Lanka (Carolio's effect) and which hit the Kerala coast, were thus of lower energy. In case the Rama Setu is broken, making a wider passage, it is feared that the waves coming into the Palk Bay, would be funneled through this passage. The funneling process would increase the intensity of the waves. Further increase would take place due to the waves propagating from south of Sri Lanka. Thus, if these waves of higher intensity were to hit the Kerala coast, the devastation would be catastrophic. The funneling effect and the destruction it can cause is noted to a certain extent at Valiazhckal on the Kerala Coast.

The India Meteorological Department has designated the Palk Bay area as a 'High Risk Area' for cyclonic activity; to this after the experience of December 2004, must be added the danger of a possible tsunami. The probability of the channel being damaged by the various natural hazards like tropical cyclones and tsunamis have not yet been worked out. Hence, proceeding with the Project, without having an idea of the quantum of money to be spent by the nation on a channel that has the potential to be damaged repeatedly by the above natural factors, might turn out to be an economic nightmare for the nation.

The cyclone season in the Bay of Bengal is generally between October to January. The records of the Meteorological Department's from 1891-2001, state that of the 452 cyclones that hit the Indian coastline, 256 were on the east coast and of these 64 have crossed the Tamil Nadu coast. Of these, 36 were 'severe cyclones' (winds in excess of 90 Kmph), 6 have crossed the Palk Bay, 14 have crossed the coast at Nagapattinam and 3 have crossed the Gulf of Mannar. All these cyclones can have a devastating consequence on the SSCP, the channel and shipping in the area.

A few more examples of the devastating consequences of these cyclones will be illustrative:

> (*i*) In Dec 1964, a cyclone washed away the Pamban Bridge.
>
> (*ii*) In Dec 1973, five metres high tidal waves hit the Palk Bay area - the very same area where the channel is to be dredged
>
> (*iii*) In Dec 1977/78, under the influence of a severe cyclonic storm that crossed the coast near Nagapattinam, 120 kmph winds were recorded in the Palk Bay area.
>
> (*iv*) In Nov/Dec 1997/98, an oil-drilling ship, anchored in the Cauvery Basin with as many as 6 anchors, broke loose from her anchors and was washed ashore by a cyclone.

(*h*) Allied to the cyclonic activity in the area, is the problem of siltation leading to a loss of sea depth. Scientists have concluded that the Palk Bay area is one of the five areas, off the Indian coast, where siltation takes place regularly. Some of their calculations have indicated a loss in sea depth of about 1 cm every year. It is pertinent to state that two of the legs of the Project, where dredging is to be undertaken, happen to cross two such micro regions where high siltation takes place.

(*i*) The foregoing will serve to illustrate the fact that cyclones and tsunamis pose a 'clear, live and present danger' to 'Safety of Lives at Sea' (SOLAS); yet the channel is sought to be created in a 'cyclone danger area'. Thus the environmental factors of cyclonic activity and siltation rates in the Palk Bay area, impinge on shipping safety.

(*j*) The REIA has also ignored the aspect of effects of tsunamis and cyclones. During the December 2004 tsunami, the entire northern leg portion (Palk Strait) of the proposed channel, had experienced tsunami waves reaching heights of more than 3.5 meters. The southern leg portion (Rama Setu) had experienced wave heights of 1.5 meters. Tsunami wave animation models by international experts have indicated excessive turbulence at Palk Bay. These factors indicate that had the channel been operational during the tsunami, its dredge dumps, its structure and its alignment would have faced very costly damage. This fact is proved right by a singular observation by various post tsunami survey teams, that the tsunami waves that had entered the Palk Bay, had dumped heaps and heaps of completely rooted out sea grasses, on the shore line of the Bay. The large-scale sedimentary deposition by this tsunami, on the coastal stretch from Kodikkarai to Cuddalore, has also made experts feel that similar deposition would have occurred at Palk Bay. All these observations warranted a detailed pre-Project study on the pattern of sedimentation experienced by Palk Bay during the last tsunami. Further, with the data generated thus, we must document the historical and pre historical tropical cyclones and tsunamis that have crossed this Project area., undertake a scientific study with inputs and collaboration from local and international oceanographic and tsunami experts to understand the effect of the current December 26th tsunami on the Project area., collaborate with the National Institute of Oceanography, Goa (which has recently proposed a scientific plan to the Government of India to conduct such a study) and identify as to how these natural hazards can affect the stability of the channel.

(k) The REIA and the clearance have overlooked the fact that India is one of the world's twelve mega diversity countries which together account for approximately 70% of the world's *biological diversity*. The Gulf of Mannar is acknowledged to be an environmentally fragile region. It is rich in endemic species : there are 3,268 species of flora and fauna present in the Gulf of Mannar and 377 species are endemic to that region. No such high level of endemism has been recorded in any other marine environment. It is considered to be one or the world's richest marine biological resources. The Gulf has been chosen as a biosphere reserve primarily because of its biological and ecological uniqueness. The group of twentyone islands in the region, has been declared as a National Marine Park by the Tamilnadu Forest Department as also the Ministry of External Affairs.

Now, with the channel, there is a danger of entry of alien species into the Gulf of Mannar and they would multiply into new areas without any control due to the absence of natural enemies; and so gradually they would crowd out the native plants and animals, degrade their habitat and contaminate the gene pools of indigenous species. Hence alien species are considered as one of the gravest threats to the bio diversity of the natural eco system worldwide.

The Gulf of Mannar is the special habitat of a marine mammal the dugong (sea cow), which has been declared a "most endangered species".The dugong migrates to Palk Bay during the South West Monsoon as, during this season, the sea in the Gulf of Mannar is rough and so feeding off sea grass beds would be difficult for it. During the North East Monsoon season, when Palk Bay becomes very turbid, it migrates from Palk Bay to the Gulf of Mannar. The dredging of the Rama Setu and movement of ships through this area would prevent movement of dugong between the Gulf of Mannar and Palk Bay. This would lead to fragmentation of its habitat and such fragmentation would lead to inbreeding and finally this may lead to extinction of this endangered marine mammal.

There are also approximately 3,600 other species of plants and animals, making the Gulf of Mannar biologically one of the richest coastal regions in India. Many of these will now be severely threatened if there is destruction of sensitive ecosystem like coral reefs and sea grass beds. One drastic effect on the Gulf of Mannar made by the Project (which involves dredging of the ocean floor near the islands), is that when it is carried into the Gulf of Mannar by ocean currents, the sedimentation from the dredging can have disastrous effect on the ecology of the whole area. This will not only kill the sensitive coral ecosystems but also affect the fisheries of the east coast, as these coral reefs are the nurseries of the major commercial fishes of India.

(*l*) The REIA and the Clearance have failed to adequately study the effect of the Project on the Gulf of Mannar. The Gulf is endowed with three marine ecosystems—those of the corals,of the sea grass beds and of the mangroves. It covers an area of 10,500 sq.km along 80° 35'N to 90° 25'N latitude and 78° 08'E to 79° 30'E longitude. There are 21 islands covering an area of 623 hectares. Most of the islands have a luxuriant growth of mangroves on their shorelines and swampy regions which are surrounded by highly productive fringing and patch coral reefs. These are sometimes referred to as underwater rain forests—a treasure house for marine ornamental fishes. The sea bottom of the inshore area around the islands, are carpeted with sea grass beds which serve as feeding ground for some highly endangered species like the dugong aforesaid. There is also great diversity of marine mammals like dolphins and whales in the Gulf's waters. Occurrence of these specialized ecosystems and the unique fauna, makes the Gulf of Mannar a marine biologist's paradise in the Indian subcontinent.

The Gulf of Mannar was declared as India's first Marine Biosphere Reserve. In fact, the Gulf of Mannar Biosphere Reserve (GOMBRE) is the first Marine Biosphere Reserve not only in India but also in South and. South East Asia. UNESCO initiated the concept of a biosphere reserve in 1971 in its Man and Biosphere (MAB) Program with the idea of oneness of humanity transcending national frontiers and recognizing the need for conservation of the vanishing species and habitats. The IUCN Commission on National Parks and WWF, identified the Reserve as being an area of particular concern given its diversity and special multiple use management status. As it is the first Marine Biosphere Reserve declared in India, this area has long been a national priority.

By G.O.M. No. 962 dated 10.09.1986, the State of Tamil Nadu notified the area under Section 35(1) of the Wildlife Protection Act, 1972; and thereafter on 18.02.1989, the Government of India set up GOMBRE. The intention to declare the 21 islands (including 3.5 fathoms depth on the Palk Bay side to 5 fathoms depth on the seaward side) as a Marine National Park for the purpose of protecting marine wildlife and its environment, is by an Act of Parliament. These islands occur in four groups namely the Mandapam group, the Keezhakaraai group, the Vembar group and the Tuticorin group. The coral reefs present in these islands are of fringing and patch types covering a distance of 140 km. Major reefs arise from the shallow sea floor not more than 5m in depth.

(*m*) There is need to study in detail possible damage to the three marine ecosystems of the Marine Biosphere—those of the corals, the sea grass beds and the mangroves.

(*i*) Coral reefs are massive limestone structures built by the primitive animals of the order Scleractinia. The reefs are centers of high biological productivity, sites of carbon dioxide sink, ecosystems that help in shoreline protection and centers of scientific research. Living coral communities generally do not grow at depths of more than 50 meters, although some grow at depths of 100 meters. Coral reef systems are very sensitive to external impact.

Annual productivity in coral reefs is about 2000-5000 gc/sq.m/yr. Such high productivity is due to efficient retention and recycling of nutrients within the ecosystem. The area of coral reef in Tamilnadu is estimated to be 94.3 sq.km. A total of 94 coral species are present in the Gulf of Mannar. Dominance of certain species is exhibited. Coral reefs lying on the southern side of the island are denser and exhibit greater species diversity than the reefs on the northern side. This is due to the constant exposure to nutrients from offshore currents. The corals provide shelter to several ornamental fishes that are found nowhere else. Some of the coral families found in India include Thamnasteriidae, Pocillioporidae and the Acoroporidae. A unique endemic species of Balanoglossus, a living fossil that is considered a link between vertebrates and invertebrates was recorded from this region.

The coral reefs system along with the ecosystem of the tropical rain forest, are the most matured marine ecosystem of our planet. They play an important role in global bio-chemical processes and in the reproduction of food resources in the tropical regions. Coral reefs also act as a barrier against wave action along the coastal areas, thus, preventing coastal erosion. In addition, coral reefs protect mangroves and sea grass beds in certain areas, which are the breeding and nursing grounds of various economically important fauna. Coral reefs are also important breeding, spawning, nesting and feeding areas for many economically important varieties of fishes and other marine organisms. Coral reefs are a distinctive shoreline habitat of stunning visual appeal, found only between latitudes 30 degree north and 30 degree south. They grow only where the sea surface temperatures are about 20 degrees Celsius, the sea bed is kept silt free by prevailing currents and waves, and there is intense surface sunlight. Living coral communities generally do not grow at depths of more than 50 meters, although some grow at depths of 100 meters. Coral reef systems are very sensitive to external impact.

(ii) Sea grasses are marine plants belonging to Monocototyledenous families. Sea grass beds are highly productive and act as breeding and nursery grounds for many epiphytic fauna and as feeding grounds of the herbivores green turtle and the sea cow. Sea grass binds sediments and prevents erosion of the 52 species of sea grass recorded worldwide, 12 species are recorded in the

Gulf of Mannar. Flow of nutrients takes place between corals and sea grass, with the aid of current enhancing the primary productivity of the sea grass. Fishes that hide in coral reefs feed in sea grass beds. Sea grasses absorb sediments thereby protecting coral reefs during storms and cyclones.

(*iii*) Mangroves are salt tolerant forest ecosystems, which support fisheries and protect the coastal zones, thus helping the marine coastal economy and environment. They are ecologically sensitive. Nine species and seven associated species are found in the Gulf of Mannar. The roots of mangrove plants have the unique habit of moving towards gravity. The leaf litter from plants, fall on the sea water, nourish the water and increase its nutrient content. This excess nutrient is food for fish fry that hatch there. Some of these plants have medicinal value. The two common mangrove species are Rhizopora sp. and Avecinia sp. These three ecosystems are interdependent in several ways. Mangroves and sea grass enhance the secondary productivity of coral reefs.

(*n*) As to the animal biodiversity of the Gulf of Mannar, this ranges in size from the microscopic planktons to the mighty whales. Dolphins are common in some parts of the Gulf. Thousands of migratory Olive Ridley sea turtles pass through the Gulf to their mass nesting in Gahirmatha in Orissa.

Contrary to the statements in the REIA, the coral reefs of the Gulf of Mannar are still rich in biodiversity and are likely to be heavily degraded by the project. Certain flagstone species that are indicators of a healthy ecosystem, like sea turtles, are still present. Dugongs though present in small numbers still can be found feeding in sea grass beds. Degradation is a natural process in a coral reef ecosystem where new corals are replaced by old ones. The corals are highly productive ecosystems and any disturbance to them could spell disaster to the fisheries in the whole of the Bay of Bengal. These act as nurseries for young fish. Migratory sea turtles like Olive Ridleys, Hawksbills, Leatherbacks, Greens and Loggerheads, are still present and these are protected by national and international laws. There are also several other endangered species.

According to research done by Monash University's Professor of Systems Ecology and UNDP Consultant, Prof. Ranil Senanayake, fresh water fish such as Dandiya (Rasbora Daniconius) and Tittaya (Amblypharygnodon Melenittus) migrate down towards underground caverns and chambers during dry weather and surface when it rains. This also demonstrates the existence of massive underground freshwater caves off Jaffna, with which the salt water of the Palk Straits would mix, if the dredging continues.

Loss to animal biodiversity can also happen in certain other ways. For example, the REIA and the Clearance fail to take into account the following facts:

(*i*) As per regulations, all ships discharge bilge water before entering the port. These normally contain eggs and live specimens of alien species that could dominate the native species.

(*ii*) Dolphins and whales will be disturbed by the traffic by ship movement since they are sensitive to ultrasonic sound waves. They could be hit by ships' propellers, leading to death.

(*o*) The Krusadai Island in the Mandapam Group of islands is of biological significance due to its diversity. This is a shallow area which is highly productive, biologically. As a consequence of the dredging, rare species of mammals (like the dugong) and fish and invertebrates such as the guitar shark and cone shells would become extinct. [Because it has become so scarce now, one cone shell (Conus Zonatus and Conus Gloria Maris) is worth around US$ 3,500.] Already reports abound of dead dugongs and whales found after dredging operations.

(p) Effect of the Project on fisheries and fisherfolk. Marine capture fisheries are the major economic activity in the Gulf of Mannar. The total area of Gulf of Mannar under the Indian Exclusive Zone is about 5,500 Sq.Km within 50 m depth. As far as fish species are concerned, of the 2,200 fish species distributed in Indian waters, 441 species have been recorded in the Gulf of Mannar. The Gulf is one of the best regions in the Indian subcontinent in fish biodiversity richness. Shore seines, boat seines, trawl nets and hook lines are the principal gear operated. The marine fish catch ranged from 55 lakh to 1.02 lakh tonnes from 1992-1996.

There are many communities of fisherfolk in the Gulf of Mannar. There are 49 villages along the coast of which 38 are in Ramanathapuram district and 11 villages are in Tuticorin district bordering the Marine Biosphere area. There are 54,000 traditional fisherfolk present in these villages out of which 14,000 are active fishermen. The average income is about Rs. 500-5000 per month. There are three fisherman's associations namely the Fisherman's Cooperative Society, the Hereditary Fisherman's Association and the Boat Owner's Association. Most of the fisherwomen are involved in seaweed collection. Chank diving is also done and is of ornamental value.

All these will be drastically impoverished both by depletion of fisheries and by closure of access of the channel area to fishermen.

(q) Economic viability is also an aspect of environmental clearance that has been ignored. There is already a well-established railway link between the various parts of the coast. Considering the biological and cultural significance of the area, especially Rama Setu, the need for a new navigational area is questionable. The fishermen in the project area are rich in cultural values.

They are traditional fishermen who cannot change their profession in a few years time. Though the fisherman's average income per month is between Rs. 500-5000, they have rich cultural value.

Also the marine resources must be utilized on a sustainable basis such there is a permanent stock for the future.

5. ERRORS IN THE ENVIRONMENTAL IMPACT ASSESSMENT REPORT

Several of the glaring wrong premises/conclusions/observations in the EIA, as reflected in the following extracts, deserved closer scrutiny but they have been uncritically accepted by the Government:

(*i*) Page No. 1.6 Para 2— The cost for the proposed canal project was worked out by PTC Ltd., based on the same quantities of dredging as in the 1983 report but with updated rates for the year 1996.

(*ii*) Page No. 1.12 Para 3— The coastal process between Arimunai (India) and Talaimannar (Sri Lanka) i.e. along Ram Seth is quite complex. These predominantly control the exchange of sediment between Gulf of Mannar and Palk Bay. Adam's Bridge is formation of submerged sand shoals and there are around 17 islands present with bushes and plants.

(*iii*) Page No. 1.14 Para 3— By this way, the entry of oceanic and alien species into the Palk Bay and the Gulf of Mannar, as also the disposal of endemic species outside die Palk Bay and the Gulf of Mannar may occur.

(*iv*) Page No. 2.37 Para 3— The area for navigation route in Adam's Bridge area was selected keeping in view the proximity to international Medial line for fishing as well as national park boundary. The purpose of selecting the stretch under study was to avoid/minimize impacts on marine national park. The selected area is approximately 10km away from Arimunai tip and about 20km away from Sringle island which is a part of national park. The bathymetry data collected in this stretch was used to identify possible alignment of route within the block. Zeroing down on to the option of 10.7m draft and 300 m width of Canal availability or creation of 12 m deep Canal with minimum dredging requirement was considered as a critical parameter to arrive at alignment across the Adam's Bridge. From the assessed bathymetry, line 2 was considered as route for navigation as dredging requirement will be minimum. This line is also at least 4 km away from medial line.

(*v*) Page No. 2.38 Para 5— The Palk Bay (PB) and the Gu.f o? ivkinn.ir (CON") are considered biologically rich and are rated among *the* highly productive seas of the world. The Gulf of Mannar harbours one of the richest biodiversity of living resources which have evolved in the past millennia.

(*vi*) Page No. 2.39 Para 1— The Gulf of Mannar has acquired ecological uniqueness, biodiversity, pluralism along with endomism. It is a natural heritage and is often called the "Biologist's Paradise".

(*vii*) Page No. 2.39 Para 2— The Gulf of Mannar is endowed with a combination of ecosystem including mangroves, seagrass and coral reefs, supporting over 3,600 species of plants and animals. It is biodiversity is considered globally significant. The Gulf of Mannar islands constitute a resting place for birds migrating to and from Sri Lanka. Approximately 168 types of birds use the islands in the Gulf as a resting place while migrating or as wintering and molting grounds. All five species of marine turtle nest in various locations in

(*viii*) On Page No. 1.6 Para 2— The cost of the proposed channel project were worked out by PTC Ltd., based on the same quantities of dredging as in the 1983 report (which, of course is quite a different alignment) but with updated rates for the year 1996. Of course these rates too are quite different from those prevailing today twelve years later.

(*ix*) On Page No. 1.12 Para 3— "The coastal process between Arimunai (India) and Talaimannar (Sri Lanks) i.e. along Adam's Bridge, which predominantly control the exchange of sediment between the Gulf of Mannar and Palk Bay, is quite complex. Rama Setu is a formation of submerged sand shoals and there are around 17 islands present with bushes and plants.

(*x*) On Page No. 1.14 Para 3— is stated: "By this way, the entry of oceanic and alien species into the Palk Bay and the Gulf of Mannar, as also the disposal of endemic species outside Palk Bay and the Gulf of Mannar, may occur." Yet no one appears to have realized how ecologically disastrous such "entry", "disposal" could be.

(*xi*) Page No. 2.37 Para 3— The site for the navigation route in the Rama Setu area, was selected keeping in view the proximity of the international medial line to fishing as well as the national park boundary. The purpose of selecting the stretch under study was to avoid/minimize impacts on the Marine National Park. The selected area is approximately 10km away from Arimunai tip and about 20km away from Sringle island which is a part of the National Park. The bathymetry data collected in this stretch was used to identify possible alignment of route within the block. Zeroing on to the option of 10.7m draft and 300 m width of channel availability or creation of 12 m deep channel with minimum dredging requirement was considered as a critical parameter to arrive at the alignment across the Adam's Bridge. From the assessed bathymetry, line 2 was considered as route for navigation as dredging requirement will be minimum. This line is also at least 4 km away from medial line.

(*xii*) Page No. 2.38 Para 5— The Palk Bay (PB) and the Gu.f o? ivkinn.ir (CON") are considered biologically rich and are rated among *the* highly productive seas of the world. The Gulf of Mannar harbours one of the richest biodiversity of living resources which have evolved in the past millennia.

(*xiii*) Page No. 2.39 Para 1— The Gulf of Mannar has acquired ecological uniqueness, biodiversity, pluralism along with endomism. It is a natural heritage and is often called the "Biologist's Paradise".

(*xiv*) Page No. 2.39 Para 2— The Gulf of Mannar is endowed with a combination of ecosystem including mangroves, seagrass and coral reefs, supporting over 3,600 species of plants and animals. It is biodiversity is considered globally significant. The Gulf of Mannar islands constitute a resting place for birds migrating to and from Sri Lanka. Approximately 168 types of birds use the islands in the Gulf as a resting place while migrating or as wintering and molting grounds. All five species of marine turtle nest in various locations in the Gulf of Mannar. Dolphins are more common here than in any other region in the Bay of Bengal. The endangered dugong uses many of the islands as browsing grounds. Marine life also includes many coloured coral fishes, eels, mollusks and stomatopoda. Sea anemones, crabs, star fish, sea urchins and numerous other organisms are found in the Gulf of Mannar waters. Page No. 2.39 Para 3. The eastern side of the islands has die greatest expanse of living coral reefs.

(*xv*) Mangroves are located on Shingle, Krusadai, Pullivasl, Poomarichan, Manoli and Manoliputti islands.

(*xvi*) Page No. 3.1 Para 1— The period of data generated belong to just before the commencement of south west monsoon.

(*xvii*) Page No. 3.2 Para 2— A survey of 20 islands in Gulf of Mannar during 1977-81 revealed the extensive destruction of fauna and flora by human interfere and require immediate action for flora and fauna (Mahadevar & Nayar, 1983).

(*xviii*) Page No. 3.15 Para 1— Pearl cysters: The proposed alignment of sethusamudaram canal passes through the groups I, VIII, XII & XIII.

(*xix*) Page No. 3.67 para 3— Varied man's activities which are, a cause for concern includes runoff and sedimentation from development activities (projects), eutrophication from sewage and agriculture, physical impact from maritime activities, dredging, collecting and destructive fishing practices, pollution from industrial sources, golf courses and oil refineries and the synergistic impacts of anthropogenic disturbance on top of natural disturbance.

(*xx*) Page No. 6.4 Para 2— The studies carried out by NSDRC signifies that the region around Adam's Bridge forms an significant sink for littoral drift. The prolonged accumulation in this area may lead to emergence of new island.

Thus the quantity of maintenance dredged spoil will increase in the Canal across Adam's Bridge in the event of cyclone.

The dredging of sea bed would result in increase of turbidity due to silt and clay both during dredging and disposal.

(*xxi*) Page No. 6.5 Para 1— Owing to the destruction of seagrass and seaweed beds, larger animals such as dugongs, turtles and herbivorous fishes are also affected. It is true that the dissolved components of the silt would enrich the algal growth and trigger the plankonic bloom. But this blooming may not be of much use since the benthic and other fauna, which mainly feed on them are either not available or destroyed owing to silt deposition.

(*xxii*) Page No. 6.12 Para 1— *Strong current would erode the banks of the canal and carry the sediments from one sector to another,* which ultimately results in accretion of sand in one sector and erosion in another sector. *Once the canal is deepened,* the passage would greatly increase die movement of fishes and other large animals from Bay of Bengal to Indian Ocean and vice versa. Hence, the entry of oceanic and alien species into Palk Bay and Gulf of Mannar and also dispersal of endemic species outside Palk Bay and Gulf of Mannar would be facilitated.

6. Summary of all the above Defects, made in two Recent Seminars in Kerala

A cross section of the academic and scientific community of Kerala represented in two seminars organized by the Centre for Innovation in Science and Social Action (CISSA), Trivandrum on the Sethu Samudram Shipping Canal Project, has debunked Government's environment clearance to the project.

The first such meeting took place at the University of Kerala, Thiruvananthapuram on 26th April 2007. This was inaugurated by Prof. (Dr.) M.K. Ramachandran Nair, Vice Chancellor of University of Kerala and attended by the Professors and Staff of the various departments. In addition, scientists from various centers also took part. The Vice Chancellor stressed the need for detailed environmental impact studies before implementing such a mega project and requested the scientific community to play a more active role.

The second meeting was organized at the School of Ocean Science and Technology, Cochin University of Science and Technology (CUSAT) on 18th October 2007 and was inaugurated by Prof. (Dr.) E.P. Yasodharan Chairman, Kearala State Council for Science, Technology and Environment. In his inaugural address the Chairman said that the cost benefits of the project does not tally with the projected economic benefits. Besides, there is also a need to carry out detailed modeling studies for assessing the impact of the proposed channel on the Kerala coast.

A large number of academic and scientific persons assembled there, including, Dr. C.S.P. Iyer, Former Director, Centre for Marine Analytical Reference & Standards, Dr. C.P. Rajendran, Centre for Earth Science Studies, Thiruvananthapuram, Prof. G.M. Nair, Professor & Head of the Department of Botany, University of Kerala, Dr. A. Biju Kumar, Dept. of Aquatic Biology and Fisheries, University of Kerala, Prof. N.R. Menon, Emeritus Professor, CUSAT, Prof. (Dr.). K.T. Damodaran, Director, School of Ocean Science & Technology, CUSAT, Prof. P. Natarajan, Rajiv Gandhi

Chair Professor, CUSAT, pointed out the lacunae in the various scientific aspects of the project. It was also unanimously decided to put before the Committee of Eminent Persons, the recommendations of the Seminars. These are summarized below:

(a) The EIA studies and TFR on the basis of which Clearance has been given for the project have not taken into account the following aspects. This is the first time in the world that a channel is being planned in mid ocean. There is no previous experience for guidance. It is not correct to make comparisons with Suez and Panama canals. Unlike these land- based canals, the proposed channel would be a part of an open sea body, subject to forces of frequent and unpredictable storms, cyclones, tsunamis and other natural hazards.

(b) The Palk Bay is an area of intense geotectonic and cyclonic activities. The GSI has classified it as zone II. Between 1891 and 2001, 64 cyclones have hit the Tamilnadu coast, out of which 36 were severe. In December 1964, one of those cyclones even washed away the Pampan Bridge.

At present, Rama Setu acts as a breakwater. Once the channel is executed cutting through the Setu, modeling studies have shown that the high energy waves of a tsunami coming from the east of India would flow through the channel in a north to south direction and also get magnified to large amplitudes by tsunamic waves coming around Sri Lanka and flowing south to north. The destruction to the south-eastern Tamil Nadu coast and to Kerala would be unimaginable. Though NEERI could not have foreseen the tsunami, which hit the Indian coast on 26th December 2004, there was a need to have a reassessment of EIA, once the event had occurred. Although tsunamis are short lived, damage caused by their impact is vast and longstanding. Proper modeling studies should be done to study the impacts of the project on the Kerala coast.

(c) The Palk Bay is an area of high sedimentation. Low wave action and protection from southerly waves encourages deposition of transported material into the Bay. No recent data has been collected on extend of sedimentation in the Bay. Even in the earlier literature, there has been no attempt to understand the sediment contribution from cyclonic storms from the Bay of Bengal or from rivers flowing into the Bay from Sri Lanka. The SCL modeling study mentioned a total quantity of 2 million tons of sediment deposition, parallel to the channel, during the monsoon. With the implementation of the project, there would be a two-fold increase in current velocities along the dredged channel. All these factors have a direct bearing on the quantum of maintenance dredging and its periodicity. More important are the integrity of the channel itself and the safety to the ship traffic, due to sedimentation.

(*d*) The Gulf of Mannar Marine Biosphere Reserve has been identified as one of the hotspots of marine biodiversity, in fact, one of the most important biodiversity reserves of the world. Major coral formations occur in this region. Nearly 3,600 species of flora and fauna including the rare ones—the sea cow, the seahorse etc. exist here. Though it is mentioned in the EIA that the channel will not affect the bioreserve, it is not supported by any data. The impact due to dredging and the oil spill caused by the ship traffic on the biota has not been documented/studied in the EIA. Long-term impacts of the Project on the rich biodiversity of the region should be studied in detail. Neither is there any mention of impacts on species included in various schedules of the Wildlife (Protection) Act.

(*e*) The proper location for the disposal of dredged material has not been evaluated. The total quantity of dredged material as per present estimates is around 82 million cubic meters - 48 million from the Rama Setu area and 34 million from Palk-Bay sector. The present plan is to dump the former in Gulf of Manner and the latter in the Bay of Bengal. Dumping these huge quantities of material in this highly turbulent area will cause turbidity and also submerge the large sea bottom community. This will have a long term ecological impact. Similarly change of currents, once the channel is a reality would cause changes in temperature, salinity, nutrients etc. This would affect the ecosystem.

(f) A major aim of the proposed project is to save ship time, fuel, transport costs and to make it attractive. This is not supported by facts and figures. Independent, realistic estimates have shown that the savings in time is insignificant for ships coming to the east coast of India from Europe and Africa; and therefore they are unlikely to use it. Moreover, due to economical reasons, the bulk carriers today are of the order of 50,000 DWT and above. These ships will not be able to use the channel with the present designed draught of 10.8 meters. This, along with increasing interest rates and the resultant uncertainty of using the channel, will make the project uneconomical.

(g) In the light of the above, it is recommended that the project should be implemented only after detailed Environment Impact Assessment The Palk Bay is an area of intense geotectonic and cyclonic activities. The GSI has classified it as Zone II. Between 1891 and 2001, 64 cyclones have hit the Tamilnadu coast, out of which 36 were severe. In December 1964, one of those cyclones even washed away the Pamban Bridge.

7. Summary of Criticisms of SSCP by Various Experts

Doubts on the technical feasibility of the Sethusamudram Shipping Channel came into limelight on January 18th, when Dr. Tad. S. Murthy, a leading international tsunami expert and a long time editor of the prestigious international tsunami journal 'Science of Tsunami Hazards', had a few important words to say, among other things, on the proposed alignment of the channel.. He said: "I like this (Sethusamudram) project, but there is a flaw. The entrance to the channel should be re-oriented towards the eastern side. Otherwise, there is a chance that it may create a deepwater route for another devastating tsunami. This may cause huge destruction in Kerala."

But, the issue is not just the alignment of the canal with respect to future tsunamis. There is much more, that has to be answered. Dr. C.P. Rajendran, a world renown geologist and paleo-seismologist at the Center for Earth Science Studies (CESS) Trivandrum, had the following to say in an interview to PTI on 27th December 2004: "I tend to believe that the environmental viability of the project is to be questioned. From an earth science point of view, I believe that the project area is highly unstable in terms of rapid sedimentation rates, high velocity ocean currents and cyclonic storms. Unless we have a clear and unambiguous understanding of the sedimentation rates along the various stretches of the Palk Bay Strait, the sustainability of the project cannot be guaranteed."

Current Science, an important Indian science journal, had published a research article on this topic in its 25 February 2005 issue. The article noted: "The current level of our understanding on the sedimentation patterns and associated dynamics existing in the segments of the Palk Strait, both during cyclone-free years and during the cyclonic years, is not adequate enough to design 'the structure and the alignment' of the canal and to draw a policy on the methods of handling the dredged material safely. The current tsunami crisis in the Bay of Bengal makes us to rethink the whole issue of our knowledge base on the geology, oceanography of this region. This note postulates, based on the above findings, that the SSCP is not feasible technically at the present moment, with the current level of understanding of the sedimentation and meteorological regimes of the project area."

The Project proponents, namely Tuticorin Port Trust (TPT) and the Ministry of Shipping and Surface Transport, chose not to participate in this debate and answer these questions in the public domain. However, when the Director of (NEERI)(which did the

Environmental Impact Analysis (EIA) and the Technical Feasibility Report (TFR) for SSCP) was questioned by the Press on March 24th 2007, he said: "The areas not covered by NEERI, were studied by others. Sediment transport was one such issue." He however did not answer as to why his organization had practically omitted the issues of cyclone and tsunami in its EIA or TFR.

Strangely, the Ministry of Environment and Forests (MoE&F), which is responsible for scrutinizing the scientific credentials of the EIA and TFR before giving an environmental clearance for the project, chose not to ask the Tuticorin Port Trust, the nodal agency, to provide answers in the public domain to all the above questions raised by the Indian scientific community. The Ministry cleared the project without much fuss in early April 2005. The Cabinet Committee and the Planning Commission chose to clear the project on May 20, 2005. The Prime Minister of India inaugurated the project on July 2, 2005.

The discussion about the scientific and technical feasibility of the project among the PMO, MoE&F, Ministry of Shipping and the Tuticorin Port Trust, was kept confidential till June 30 night, that is till one day before the Project inauguration. The website of the Sethusamudram Corporation (www.sethusamudram.gov.in) was launched on that day and was notified to the public on July 1 2005.

The website carries the responses that the Tuticorin Port Trust had given to the PMO to the questions raised from January to early March 2005, on the technical feasibility of the project.

The Government itself has published a Manual on how the Environment Impact Assessment is to be prepared, and has ignored those very guidelines.

Dr. Ramesh writing in *Current Science*/Vol. 88, No. 4, 25 February 2005] addressed some of the short-term as well as the long-term implications of this project *from the existing database* raising some relevant questions on the technical feasibility of the project, which questions seem to have been overlooked by the Project impact assessment studies sponsored by the Central Government.

At the risk of repetition, Dr. Ramesh's arguments are set out below. He argues that the navigation channels near the ports of the east coast *have* been facing three major problems persistently. These are caused mainly by natural sedimentation, tropical cyclones, and the dumping of the dredged material. SSCP cannot be an exception to these problems and these issues could be more complicated by the fact that the Project area occurs in the offshore. The central issue, therefore, is whether these issues have been adequately addressed before embarking on this venture.

Interestingly previous studies have indicated sedimentation activity at the rate of 29 m/yr in the Vedaranyam-Jaffna stretch of the Palk Bay, to such an extent that it is possibile that in another 400 years there will develop a land connection between Vedaranyam and the Jaffna peninsula. Moreover, it should be noted that the two legs of the SSCP where dredging is required, coincide with two such zones with high sedimentation rates.

In addition to these routine sedimentation dynamics, the canal project area is also threatened by cyclones; sixty four cyclones have been known to have hit the Tamil Nadu Coast between 1891 and 2000. Out of these, 36 (55%) were severe cyclonic storms (wind speed exceeding 89 km/hour). Twenty three storms have crossed the project area in the above-mentioned period. Based on the storm surge values (3-5 m), the India Meteorological Department considers the coastal stretch between Nagapattinam and Pamban (the canal project area) as a high risk zone. For example, the cyclone of 23rd December 1964 had produced a storm surge that submerged Dhanushkoti town! Based on the degree of uncertainly in the prior prediction of cyclones, Dr. Ramesh terms this coastal stretch (and that of Bangladesh) as the most vulnerable among the many regions along the Bay of Bengal. The exact role of cyclones in influencing the sedimentation pattern has not been studied in detail; however, it has been noted that these storms have a tendency to transport sediments into the Palk Bay from the Nagapattinam Coast and from the Gulf of Mannar. An analysis of the data on the extent of shoreline oscillation of the Tamil Nadu Coast suggests that the southern part of the Palk Bay is accretionary, throughout the year, whereas the northern part experiences both erosion and accretion. Accretionary tendency is greater during the southwest monsoon (June to August), and it is lower (or erosion is high) during the northeast monsoon (October to January). The project impact studies have ignored the issues related to cyclones, completely.

Another concern is the degree of turbidity that will be generated during the process of dumping of dredged material and its impact on fishing. The current level of our understanding on the sedimentation patterns and associated dynamics existing in the segments of the Palk Strait both during cyclonic-free years and during the cyclonic years is not adequate enough to design 'the structure and the alignment' of the canal and to draw a policy on the methods of handling the dredged material safely. The current tsunami crisis in the Bay of Bengal makes us to rethink the whole issue of our knowledge base on the geology and oceanography of this region. This Dr. Raman postulates, based on his findings, that the SSCP is not feasible technically (questions have also been raised, on the economic viability of the project, in Chapter 4 here) at the present moment with the current level of understanding of the sedimentation and meteorological regimes of the project area.

As pointed out earlier, for the SSCP, the environmental Clearance was issued by the Government in August 2004. It predated the tsunami. On December 26, 2004, a Tsunami wave entered the Palk Strait sea strip between India and Sri Lanka, to gain strength and fury as it funneled through the narrow straits. But it met something that the wave did not expect: the Ram Setu. This chain of coral islets made of rock and sand deflected the tidal wave back into open sea. The wave was hence forced to find a route around Sri Lanka and by the time it reached coastal Kerala on the other side, it had lost much of its potency and speed.

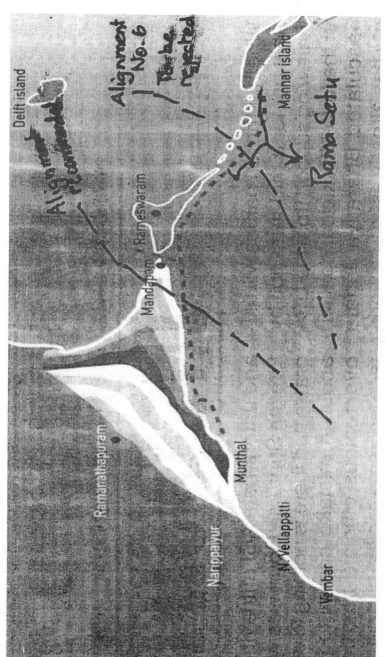

Figure 8

"That chain of coral islets saved coastal Kerala that day. "That is the view of Prof. Tad Satyam Murthy, former president of the International Tsunami Society and a tsunami consultant to the Indian government, now living in Canada as a Professor. (See Annexure 10 & 11)

The Sethusamudram project which is about breaking this bridge of islets to make way for a channel linking the Bay of Bengal to the Gulf of Mannar, therefore could be a dangerous. Many scientists too from different disciplines say not enough research has been done on the Tsunami angle before starting this project.

Geologists also say there are active volcanoes and moving tectonic plates in the region. Ecologists claim the bridge checks the rough seas of the Bay of Bengal to create a haven for marine life. Mariners argue the proposed channel is a disaster management nightmare. If a ship runs aground, there is no system in place to extricate it and clear the channel. Scientists formerly associated with organizations such as the Geological Survey of India (GSI) and Indian Rare Earths wonder why their organizations have not been consulted on this project at all!

Scientists such R. Gopalakrishnan, former GSI director, and non-governmental organizations are agitated because no detailed post-tsunami studies have been done.

In fact a week after the Project was finalized, it ran into the tsunami. Two months after the tsunami, Project authorities sent a registered letter to Murthy, who lives in Canada and teaches at the University of Ottawa to consult him. He opined that if another tsunami strikes, this proposed channel would cause devastation on the Kerala coast: "In the 2004 tsunami, no significant amount of tsunami energy traveled to Kerala through the waters between India and Sri Lanka. The water had to take a wide turn around Sri Lanka. In this process, the water missed southern Kerala. However, if the Sethu Canal is widened and deepened, this will provide an alternative route for the Indonesian tsunamis to funnel energy into the channel." His recommendation was clear: the threat is real, realign the channel. He also offered his services to create a computer simulation of his theory. No one has taken him up on it.

N.K. Raghupathy, the former chairman of SCL who was asked to go on leave in July, 2007 and was transferred from his post in September 2007 told: "When I left (in July), we had been thinking about forming a team to look into the tsunami angle," he added. But no such team has been formed so far.

The report, compiled by the National Environmental Engineering Research Institute (NEERI), Nagpur, was based on raw data provided by S. Kathiroli, Director of the National Institute of Ocean Technology (NIOT). As it turns out, Kathiroli was also on the board of the Dredging Corp. of India (DCI) when he was director of NIOT. After the project was approved, DCI got the contract for dredging the channel for the Rs. 2,600 crore project, a possible conflict of interest that this dual directorship may have created.

Kathiroli's Report said there was no rock on the Ram Setu! However, in January, 2007 a dredger hit a rock bed and broke its spud.

Since it is impossible to simply cut through the rock layers of Ram Sethu, it is reported that the solution the government had come up with was to use explosives. However if there was any such plan, the government had to abandon it quickly. In the last week of August, the Supreme Court heard of the rumours through a petition filed by this author and issued an special order asking the government not to damage any part of Ram Sethu until the case is disposed off.

Even if the Supreme Court issues a verdict allowing the blasting, NEERI has threatened to withdraw its approval. "Our report cleared it without the blasting. The region is a marine biosphere. There are many Schedule-1 species in the area. Any blasting will destroy its (the area's) fragile ecology. We simply cannot, cannot risk it," says S. Wate, one of the authors of the NEERI report opined.

Dr. N.S. Areeba Hamid, oceans campaigner of Greenpeace India, says the Gulf of Mannar, with over 3,600 known species of fauna and flora, is home to rare and endangered species. "The biodiversity of this region is already under threat. We need to keep away threats like the Sethu project," she says.

Otherwise, *it will not be as much the case that the SSCP will wreck the environment but that the environment will ruin the SSCP.* It may be Nature's desire to keep the Palk Straits shallow, and therefore to tamper with nature requires first propitiating Mother Nature.

CHAPTER 7

Conclusion

My study of the economics of the SSCP rejects the choice of Alignment No. 6 as a financial white elephant, and perhaps a milch cow for some corrupt politicians and bureaucrats and instead suggests consideration for fresh evaluation of the whole concept of a ship channel as a method of development of the Tuticorin Port and the Tamil Nadu coastal areas. There are alternative projects such a rail lines connected to container ports to be considered.

If SSCP is to be implemented, then Alignment No. 1, through Mandappam, is preferable from all angles – economics, environment, and national security – to the current choice of Alignment No. 6 (Figure No. 5). This Alignment No. 1 was in fact originally suggested after Independence by Ramaswami Mudaliar Committee but the Government then did not regard it as economically viable. If this alignment also cannot be accepted for any reason even today, then it is better in the national interest to scrap the SSCP altogether, and recover the sunk costs by attaching the immovable property and assets of those in authority who had pushed it through hastily and in reckless disregard of the historicity of the Rama Setu, the economic unviability, the environment disaster, and the national security risks of the Project, had designed the SSCP based on Alignment No. 6 as the channel route, a choice that betrays besides our ancient civilization and Sanatan Dharma, and thus willfully commits sacrilege by providing for the destruction of the holy Rama Setu.

Hence, it is essential now to set up an independent multi-disciplinary investigative committee of experts to rectify this serious lapse on part of NEERI by re-examining all six Alignments ab initio in light of new data and issues, and recommend a final considered choice, if any, or any alternative projects to meet the multi-dimensional concerns of the nation as well as frame an effective security policy for safeguarding the environment.

In framing effective security policies for the SSCP, the complexities of international shipping need also to be understood. A ship is built in one country, has a flag of convenience of a second country, is owned by a national of a third country and the vessel itself is manned by a crew of mixed nationalities with differing security clearance standards, is controlled through the Flag State in all its internal matters, but is subject to local Port State jurisdiction! The global terrorist is aware, that, apart from a few international agreements with respect to slavery, piracy and illicit carriage of narcotics, there is no comprehensive Maritime Law to combat Maritime Terrorism. The terrorist can and does take advantage of this legal vacuum. There are diverse, complex and often conflicting domestic laws enacted by different coastal States.

If the foregoing was bad enough, consider the Indian scene. The Indian Navy and Coast Guard come under the Ministry of Defence. Fisheries come under the Ministry of Agriculture. DG Shipping/DG lighthouses come under the Ministry of Shipping. The customs come under the Revenue Wing of the Ministry of Finance. ONGC comes under the Ministry of Petroleum. Also, the nodal agency for dealing with any marine oil spill is the Coast Guard. However, the nodal Ministry for oil spills is the Home Ministry. There can be no co-ordination in such a situation of crossed-wires.

Hence, we need to take a leaf out of the U.S. Homeland security *Blue Book*. The U.S. Coast Guard is the Single Nodal Agency for maritime aspects of their Homeland Security. In special cases, the U.S. Navy can also discharge the responsibilities of even the Coast Guard. U.S. laws provide for such an eventuality.

Hence, we too need to enact new "Maritime Security" laws with a single nodal agency to counter the threats of piracy or armed robbery at sea as also Maritime Terrorism. National security is too serious not to override the States rights, federalism and parochial politics.

The recent Government-appointed so-called *Committee of Eminent Persons for the Sethusamudram Ship Channel Project* has forfeited public confidence because of bias and sycophancy.

The Chairman of this Government-appointed Committee, Dr. S. Ramachandran is shown, in the photo below garlanding and placing a silk angavastram on Mr. M. Karunanidhi Chief Minister of Tamil Nadu, when the latter sat on a 'fasting' protest against the Supreme Court Order declaring the Bandh call given by the CM as illegal and violative of the citizens' Fundamental Rights. The Bandh had been called originally to protest against the Supreme Court Order of August 31, 2007 on my Petition, granting injunction against the Project damaging the Rama Setu in any way. What objectivity can this Chairman exercise when he, and that too on such an occasion, exhibits such unabashed and disgusting sycophancy to a Chief Minister committed to destroying the Rama Setu?

Annexure 1

RAPID ENVIRONMENT IMPACT ASSESSMENT
(SEPTEMBER 2002)

In the year 2002, Tuticorin Port Trust appointed NEERI as consultants for carrying out Rapid & Comprehensive Environment Impact Assessment Studies along with assessing Techno-economic viability of the project. The objective of the study was to obtain Environmental Approvals from the concerned local, state, and central government authorities. The terms of Reference issued by TPT to NEERI comprises of two section viz. Techno-economic viability & other related to Environment Impact Assessment as given below:

TOR for Techno-economic viability
- Establishment of Techno-economic viability of the project
- Collection of oceanographic and meterological data
- Estimation of quantum of capital dredging
- Suggestion of best suited dredging methods, dumping & disposal methods
- Spell out offshore & onshore disposal areas
- Assessment of quantum of maintenance dredging periodicity & disposal areas
- Furnish requirement of onshore facilities for administration

The progress report discussed about the project setting, baseline environmental conditions in terms of marine, land and social-economic environments.

Further the report also discussed about the impacts for the construction and operation phases.

TOR for Environmental Impacts Assessment
- Short listing of viable routes based on Techno-economical considerations
- Assessment of present status of coastal water, marine, land, biological and socio-economic components including parameters of human interest
- Identification of potential impacts on various environmental components due to activities envisaged during construction and operation phases of the project
- Prediction of impacts using various simulation models
- Preparation of Environmental Impact Statement

- Delineation of acceptable Channel route for shipping based on environmental considerations
- Delineation of Environmental Management Plan
- Enumeration of benefits due to ship movements in the operation phase of the Channel
- Formulation of environmental quality monitoring programme for construction and operation phases
- Make a presentation of the EIA Reports to various government agencies, environment authorities of State Government, NGO's, MoEF etc.

Subsequently NEERI submitted a progress report to Tuticorin Port Trust in September 2002 on the works carried out till then. Observations on this report are as follows:

- The progress report submitted by NEERI in September 2002 discussed about the present environment status in terms of marine, land & socio-economic environments, Environment impacts & Channel alignment and Techno-economic viability. The study area was the same as considered in IEE.
- The report presented the environmental setting of the project area in terms of the island details in Gulf of Mannar, Hydrography etc. But details pertaining to access & site surrounding, access to Adam's Bridge etc have not been discussed.
- The present status of the marine environment was established by drawing on the data collected during the IEE in 1998. The data presented for the Marine Environment covered the Physico-chemical and biological status. The assessment covered the marine water and sediment. The analysis given for the various marine environmental components is laudable and confirms the biodiversity richness of the Gulf of Mannar and Palk Bay.
- The status of land environment was established by using satellite imageries by developing false colour composites using IRC LISS & PAN images. The data was further used for identifying suitable sited for disposal of dredged material.
- The socio-economic environment elaborately discussed about the profile of the fishing communities located around Gulf of Mannar and Palk Bay. The profile was arrived at by analysis of secondary/published data supported with a rapid sample survey representing 8000-10000 fishermen hailing from Pamban, Natarajapuram, Ramakrishnapuram, Kothandaramakoil Nagar and Moonruerupuchattram. During the random survey, the public perception about the project was eliciated.
- The impact associated with the project were discussed in terms of:
  - Land acquisition, Rehabilitation & Resettlement, Impacts due to Dredging/Dredged material disposal, Increased Road/Rail Traffic, Socio-economic impacts, Ecological impacts and Hydrodynamics Aspects.

- Analysis of Alternatives – The various alignment suggested during various studies were analysed in content of technical, economical, environmental and social aspects and alignment along the Adams Bridge has been accordingly finalized.
- On finalisation of the alignment, Techno-economic viability studies were carried out covering traffic, economics and benefits.

It is understood that the progress report is basically meant for finalising the Channel alignment paving way for further studies.

Annexure 2

ENVIRONMENT IMPACT ASSESSMENT
(SEPTEMBER 2003)

This report is an upgraded version of the progress report submitted by NEERI in September 2002. This report, Rapid Environmental Impact Assessment Report, has been prepared using the available baseline data (similar to the one in Progress report & IEE), preparation of environmental impact statement based on identification, prediction, evaluation of impacts, ranking of environmentally viable alternatives and preparation of environmental management plan along with environmental monitoring programme. The observations on the report are as follows:

- The hydrographic data pertaining to tides, currents, sediment transport has been analysed from available secondary data /published literature. Tidal observations were made at Pamban Port between 3rd May to 5th May, 2003.
- Baseline marine environment status has been established by using the data generated during the IEE in 1998 and the same was validated by resampling at the locations. The marine environmental status was established for Adams Bridge, Palk Bay & Gulf of Mannar. The marine environment data related to fishing reported availability of fish in shallow waters near Dhanushkodi within 2 to 3 ft.
- The information presented for marine environment is comprehensive and covers components related to marine environment.
- The landuse cover/ landuse data was presented for Pamban Island. The data generated by using IRCC LIS satellite images in 1998 were revalidated and checked by using the Satellite Imageries procured in May 2002. The area suitable for disposal of dredged spoil has been identified using this data. The land identified for dredged material disposal is located between Kodandaramaswamy Temple & Dhanushkodi.
- The impacts associated with the project have been discussed for Pre-construction, Construction and Post Construction Phases. The impacts were analysed using network methods.
- Impacts on the marine environment were mainly studied in terms of sediment transport/littoral movement using hydrodynamic models. The

impacts were focused mainly on the marine environment. The impacts due to development of shore based facilities, road/rail movement, land acquisition and R&R issues were qualitatively discusses. The positive benefits especially on the economic front were not much focused.

- The Environmental Management Plan presented in this stage of report was indicative but addressed most of the issues. The EMP did not discuss about the monitoring requirements related to construction and operation phases and also about the required institutional mechanism.

Annexure 3

Sethusamudram
CORPORATION LIMITED

ENVIRONMENTAL IMPACT ASSESSMENT FOR
PROPOSED SETHUSAMUDRAM SHIP CHANNEL PROJECT

by

National Environmental Engineering Research Institute
Nehru Marg, Nagpur - 440 020
August 2004

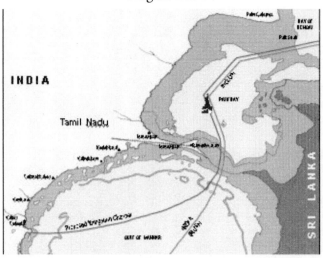

INTRODUCTION

India does not have, within her own territorial waters, a continuous navigable route around the peninsula due to the presence of a shallow (1.5 to 3.5 m depth) ridge called 'Adam's Bridge' between Pamban island on south-eastern coast of India and Talaimannar of Sri Lanka. While Rameshwaram is a major pilgrim centre on Pamban island, the tip of the island is marked by Arimunai. Consequently, the ships calling at ports on the east coast of India have to go around Sri Lanka entailing an additional distance of about 254-424 nautical miles and about 21-36 hours of ship time.

The Sethusamudram Ship Channel Project under the consideration of the Ministry of Shipping, Government of India, envisages creation of a ship navigation channel to suit different draughts (9.15 m, 10.7 m and 12.8m) through dredging/ excavation in Adam's Bridge, parts of Palk Bay and Palk Strait. The navigation route will originate from the Tuticorin new harbour in the Gulf of Mannar (GOM) using available navigation depths (> 20 m) up to south east of Pamban Island, pass through a channel created in Adams Bridge within the International boundary and proceed parallel to the International Medial Line for fishing rights as the Bengal Channel. In Palk Bay area availability of depths in middle channel, capital dredging across Adams Bridge and in Palk Strait and continuous maintenance dredging along the proposed transit are the critical project related issues.

The routes selected through earlier studies particularly in Gulf of Mannar area have been rejected, keeping in view sensitivity along the coastal stretch of GOM harbouring marine national park. Instead a navigation route keeping a minimum 6-8 km distance from Van Tiu near Tuticorin and more than 20 km from Shingle in Adams Bridge approach area has been suggested.

Tuticorin Port Trust (TPT), the nodal agency identified by Ministry of Shipping, Govt. of India for the implementation of the project in pursuance of its decision to incorporate environmental considerations in the design phase of the project, retained, in March 2002, National Environmental Engineering Research Institute (NEERI) to conduct the Environmental Impact Assessment (EIA) study for the project.

This report presents briefly the project setting, describes the baseline environmental status of the project area, identifies environmental issues, predicts and evaluates impacts due to the proposed project and delineates environmental management plan to mitigate potential adverse impacts.

The EIA study has primarily drawn upon the available information on the proposed project, the hydrography, marine water quality and ecological resources in the project area, and the primary data generated during the course of study. This environmental impact assessment study with intensive data collection has resulted into fuller description and appreciation of the natural processes occurring in the study area, and delineates the environmental consequences including the ecological risk associated with the proposed project with or without proper environmental management plan.

PROJECT

The proposed Sethusamudram ship channel will have two legs, one near the Point Calimere called the Bay of Bengal Channel and the other across the Adams Bridge. The Bay of Bengal Channel traverses the Palk Bay wherein the sea-bed is mostly soft to hard clayey-sand in nature. Some hard strata has been reported beneth the soft sand during recent survey by the National Hydrographic Office, Dehradun. The area adjoining Adma's Bridge, Dhanushkody Peninsula on the North and the

South is reported to be sandy by National Ship Design Research Centre (NSDRC), Visakhapatnam during their survey in connection with this project.

While navigational depths will be used in Gulf of Mannar from Tuticorin Port to Adam's Bridge area, a 20 km long, 300 m wide channel with 10.7 m draught with two way controlled traffic is proposed to be created as ultimate phase by dredging shallow area of Adam's Bridge upto 12 m depth. Similar excavation will be done in Palk Strait and adjoining parts of Palk Bay to achieve the required depth over a stretch of around 36 km and 18 km respectively. A control station, administrative building and Vessel Traffic Management System (VTMS) is proposed to be located at Rameswaram island between Dhanushkodi and Koil Nagar village to control navigation, besides other infrastructure including administrative requirements.

ENVIRONMENTAL REGULATIONS

At the National level, the environmental clearance to the project is subject to compliance with the stipulated safeguards under the provisions of Environment (Protection) Act, 1986; Forest (Conservation) Act, 1980; The Water (Prevention and Control of Pollution) Act, 1974; The Water (Prevention and Control of Pollution) Rules, 1975; The Water (Prevention and Control Pollution) Cess Act, 1977. The Water (Prevention and Control of Pollution) Act, 1981; and other rules and regulations in force. Land use on the coastline will be subject to regulation as per the Coastal Regulation Zone (CRZ) Notification issued by the Ministry of Environment and Forests (MoEF), Government of India in 1991 and subsequent amendments under the Environmental Protection Act. This notification is administered by the State Department of Environment and Forests.

The Wildlife (Protection) Act of India (1972) provides legal protection to many marine animals including reef associated organisms. Chapter IV of this Act dealing with Sanctuaries, National Parks etc. is equally applicable to marine reserves, marine national parks and biosphere reserves.

The Gulf of Mannar Marine Biosphere Reserve (GOMMBR) has been notified in 1989 through an executive communication from the Secretary to the Government of India, Ministry of Environment and Forests to the Chief Secretary, Government of Tamil Nadu.

During the operational phase of the project, the most important instrument to be complied relates to the International Convention for the Prevention of Pollution from Ships 1973 as modified by the Protocol of 1978 (MARPOL 73/78) for which India is a signatory.

KEY FINDINGS

Environmental Status

MARINE ENVIRONMENT

The Palk Bay and the Gulf of Mannar covering an area of 10,500 sq. km in which the proposed ship channel is to be created are biologically rich and rated among the highly productive seas of the world. Its diversity is considered globally significant. In the Gulf of Mannar, between the coast line and the proposed alignment, there are 21 islands which have been declared as National Marine Parks by the Tamil Nadu Forest Department and the MoEF, Government of India. While the proposed channel alignment in the Tuticorin Port area shall be about 6 km from Van Tiu the nearest island, in Adam's Bridge area it will be about 20 km from Shingle Island which is a part of National Marine Park.

The data on physico-chemical characteristics and marine biological resources was collected from various sampling stations in Gulf of Mannar and Palk Bay. Primary data on physico-chemical characteristics of marine water shows no significant variation in alkalinity (102-106 mg/l) and pH (8.0-8.2) along the proposed channel alignment. The DO values varied from 3.2 to 5.7 mg/l and the silicates from 0.003 mg/l to 0.017 mg/l. No significant variation in salinity is observed between surface and bottom samples. An inverse relationship between salinity and silicates has been observed. The nitrate concentrations vary from 0.78 mg/l to 1.1 mg/l. Data from secondary sources in coastal areas of Palk Bay near Palk strait shows pH ~ 8.2, D.O. 5.8-6.5 mg/l and Total nitrogen content of 0.4 mg/l.

Sediment samples collected along the proposed channel alignment show the presence of organic carbon, total nitrogen, total phosphorous and sulphates in concentrations adequate for biological growth. Almost all the sediment samples show presence of oil & grease. The concentrations of heavy metals are high in some of the sediments in the Palk Bay as compared to other locations.

Biological Resources

The gross primary productivity along the proposed channel alignment vary from 142 to 472 mgC/m^3/day indicating that the Gulf of Mannar and the Palk Bay are biologically productive regions. The zooplankton are dominated by copepod. Macrobenthos represented by 78 varieties exhibit fairly good diversity. The meiofauna comprised larval polychaetes, nematodes and worms.

The corals along the proposed channel alignment in Adam's Bridge do not exist though major groups of biological resources like sea fan, sponges, pearl oysters, chanks and holothuroids at various sampling points have been recorded. In general, the density of economically/ecologically important species along the proposed alignment is not significant.

All the three groups of prochordata organisms, considered as the connecting link between invertebrates and vertebrates, viz., hemichordata, cephalochordata and urochordata comprising 1, 6 and 59 species respectively have been recorded around the islands of the Gulf of Mannar.

There are 87 fish landing stations between the south of Point Calimere and Pumban in the Palk Bay, and 40 stations in the Gulf of Mannar between Pamban and Tuticorin. Out of over 600 varieties of fishes recorded in this area, 200 are commercially important. During 1992-1996, the fish production has increased gradually from 55,325 tonnes in 1992 to 2,05,700 tonnes in 2001.

Biodiversity

Non-conventional fishing in the region is represented by pearl, chank, sea weeds, ornamental shells and holothurians. There has been a declining trend in the production of these organisms as evidenced by the revenue received by MPEDA.

Rare and endangered species of sea turtle, dolphin, sea cow and whale are recorded in the Gulf of Mannar and the Palk Bay. The sea cow inhabitates the shallow shore regions where grasses occur, while other endangered animals mostly prefer deep sea.

Several species of green algae (32), brown algae (35), red algae (59), blue green algae (3) and sea grasses are recorded in the Gulf of Mannar and the Palk Bay. A few of the 21 islands are reported to possess patches of mangroves predominated by *Avicennia* sp. And *Rhizophora* sp.

Most of the habitats of the sensitive biota, viz., corals, pearl oysters, chanks, sea cow, holothuroids and marine algae are along the coast and around the 21 islands, and mostly away from the proposed canal alignment.

Point calimore wild life sanctuary sprawling over 17.26 sq. km. Area comprising tidal swamp, dry evergreen forests and mangroves is located in coastal areas of Palk strait in Nagapattinam District. The sanctuary is bestowed with population of varied wildlife such as Chital, Wild Bear, Bannet, Macaque, Black Buck, Flamingoes, Teals, Gulls Tems, Plovers and Stilts, Dolphins and Turtles are seen close to shore area.

Land Environment

Based on an analysis and interpretation of IRS IC LISS-III satellite data, merged with PAN data, degraded area in Pamban island has been delineated for anticipated disposal of dredged material to the extent possible with prior approval under CRZ regulations. A large stretch about 753 hectare, of such land between Rameshwaram and Dhanushkody is available.

There are no archaeologically significant structures along the proposed channel alignment. However, there are apprehensions of encountering cultural/ archaeological artifacts during the excavation of the channel though borehole data generated by the National Ship Design Research Centre (NSDRC) does not support such a situation.

Socio-economic Environment

Along the coast in the Gulf of Mannar and the Palk Bay there are 138 villages and towns belonging to 5 districts. The socio-economic profile of the fishermen in the villages of Gulf of Mannar coast is low, and more than 40% of families are in debt.

The local people are of concern that the creation of channel would result in the reduction of their income due to fishery.

Oceanographic Status

The hydrodynamic studies of the seabed in Adam's Bridge and its adjoining area have been carried out in May 2003 and February 2004 by retaining the services of National Ship Design Research Centre (NSRDC), Vishakhapatnam. The hydrographic charts bearing nos. 1584, 1586, 1587, 2069, 2197 and 96 have been referred while conducting the surveys.

There are two circulations of water masses observed in the Bay of Bengal, the clockwise circulation in south-west monsoon and the counter clockwise circulation in the north-east monsoon. The tidal variations are between 0.05 to 0.7 m. The current velocities in the Palk Bay and the Gulf of Mannar are as mild as 0.2 - 0.4 m/s except on few days during south-west monsoon when it rises upto 0.7 m/s. Water currents follow the directions of predominant winds. The analysis of current data shows no potential threats to siltation of channel. It is observed that during southwest monsoon the sediments move from Gulf of Mannar to Palk Bay and during fair weather the direction reverses. In annual cycle, a net exchange of 6000 m³ of sediment is found to move from Palk Bay to Gulf of Mannar through Pamban pass and 25000 m³ of sediment moves from Gulf of Mannar to Palk Bay through Arimunai.

Geological strata in Adam's Bridge area shows soft and hard sand upto 12 m with particle size varying from 65 to 600 mm. The bathymetry varies from 0.6 to 6.3 m. Depth in Palk strait averages to about 8 m.

The hydrographic survey of Palk Bay and Palk strait area has been carried out during Jan. 25 - Feb. 18, 2004 by the Naval Hydrographic Department of National Hydrographic Office (NHO). According to the findings of NHO, the seabed in this region comprises of sand and mud with few broken shells. The depth contours in the sea are in agreement with those depicted on the existing navigational chart No. 358. While navigable depth (more than 12 m) will be used in about 78 km stretch in Palk Bay, a sizable stretch (about 54 km) will require to be dredged in Palk Strait and adjoining area. Sub bottom profile studies indicate that though the upper layer of sediment is made up of mud and sand, there is some hard strata under the soft sediment. This hard strata if discovered to be rock, if would require blasting at the time of dredging to achieve the desired draught.

The tides in the area are not similar. Both semi-diurnal and diurnal tides are observed at the tidal station set up. The range of spring tides vary between 0.4 to 0.7 m. The current in the area is N-S direction with speeds varying from 0.08 to 0.8 m/s and may reach 1.8 m/s (4 kt) in spring. No wrecks and obstruction have been observed during the survey.

IMPACTS DUE TO THE PROJECT

Impacts on Landbased Facilities

The project envisages construction of shore facilities to cater the needs of channel in Adam's Bridge area, viz. service jetties, slipways, buoy yard, repair workshop as also staff and administration buildings for facilitating regulated traffic in the vicinity of Adam's bridge area. The locations of land-based structures, and the extent of area required for their construction is required to be identified on Pamban island in consultation with local authorities. Most of the land east of Rameshwaram is barren and covered by sand and scant vegetation. There are few hamlets at Arimunai and Dhanushkodi who are engaged in fishing. These fisherman will be displaced in the event the land based facilities are planned in this area. Temporary displacement of these fisherman is envisaged. A BSF check post will also be temporarily affected. Land on Pamban island has also been identified for disposal of dredged material (silt/clay/sand). The land cover, landuse as also the ownership of sites required for the project related activities will be firmed up once the modus-operendi of traffic regulation in channel is finalized. Hence, the extent of land acquisition, the need for resettlement and rehabilitation of affected population, if any, can not be assessed at this juncture. However, given the fact that channel will cut across the Adam's Bridge area, the impacts on land based facilities would be negligible in comparison to that envisaged in earlier studies where land locked canal cutting through Pamban Island was proposed.

During the construction of the ship channel, it is anticipated that considerable sea-borne activity in the form of logistic and support services would take place. This would have significant adverse impact on the traditional fishing activities by the licensed fisher folk and consequently on their income levels.

Impacts on Productivity and Ecology in GOM/Palk Bay

As the proposed alignment in Gulf of Mannar is more than 20 km away from the existing 21 islands in National Marine Parks in the Gulf of Mannar, the marine biological resources around these islands will not be affected to any significant level.

The existing level of primary productivity in the project area will remain practically unaltered during the construction and operation phases of the channel. There would not be any significant change in water quality including turbidity due to the proposed deployment of cutter suction/trailor suction hopper dredgers for capital and maintenance dredging.

Due to dredging the bottom flora and fauna on an area about 6 sq. km along the channel alignment in Adams Bridge and about 16-17 sq.km in Palk Bay/Palk Strait area will be lost permanently. This loss, however, will be very insignificant compared to the total area of 10,500 sq. km of the Gulf of Mannar Marine Biosphere Reserve.

In Adam's Bridge area about 38 million m³ of dredge spoil comprising about 7-8 million m³ clay silt will be generated for achieving 12 m depth for 300 m wide channel including allowances for slope and tolerance. It is proposed that spoil containing a mixture of clay and sand will be disposed on degraded areas of Pamban island for reclaiming the land subject to approval of Forest and Environment Department (TN) for use of area falling under CRZ as dumping of wastes in CRZ area is not permissible activity. Balance 30 million m³ spoil containing mainly sand (particle size 125 mm to 600 mm) will be discharged in sea 25 km away from the dredging area keeping safe distance from medial line at depths varying from 30-40 m to minimise the impact. In the event of restricting the channel to 10 m depth to suit vessels with 9.15 m draught, the quantity of dredged spoil will reduce by 13.5 million m³ and material required to be disposed in sea will be 16-17 million m³ instead of 30 million m³ as envisaged for 12 m depth. This would further minimize impacts on sea bed due to disposal of dredged spoil.

In Palk Bay area, about 44 million m³ of dredged spoil will be generated due to excavation activity in Palk strait and Palk Bay to achieve 12 m depth for 300 m channel including allowances for slope and tolerance. The NHO data indicate hard strata beneth soft sand hence spoil may contain silt, sand and hard material. The dredging may also require blasting if hard strata is encountered. In the event of blasting, adverse impact on sea bottom fauna is envisaged. The spoil is proposed to be discharged in Bay of Bengal at suitable depth (25-40 m) to minimize impacts on coastal areas of Palk Bay. An option of using silt/clay for beach nourishment is also recommended. In the event of restricting the channel depth to 10 m the requirement of dredging in Palk Bay/Palk strait will drastically reduce to about 14.8 million m³ as against 44 million m³ envisaged for 12 m depth. This would minimize environmental impacts as well cost of dredging and disposal.

It would be ideal to explore the possibility of dredging the channel to 10 m depth in first phase to cater to vessels of 9.15 m draught and monitor environmental status during construction and operation phases. The proposal of 12.0 m depth can subsequently be taken up in second phase provided adverse impacts on environment are not observed.

Hydrodynamic modelling studies using Depth Integrated Velocity and Solute Transport (DIVAST) model have shown that, even for the highest spring tidal water conditions, there will be no significant change in the magnitude and direction of current velocities along the proposed alignment due to the construction of the channel in Adam's bridge area.

During the construction and operation phases of the channel, the potential sources of marine pollution are spillage of oil and grease, marine litter, jetsam and floatsam including plastic bags, discarded articles of human use from the sea-borne vessels which will have to be controlled.

The channel may facilitate the movement of fishes and other biota from the Bay of Bengal to the Indian Ocean and vice versa. By this way, the entry of oceanic and alien species into the Palk Bay and the Gulf of Mannar, as also the dispersal of endemic species outside the Palk Bay and the Gulf of Mannar could occur.

Socio-economic Impact

The channel will establish a continuous navigable sea route around peninsular coast within the Indian territorial waters, reduce shipping distance by about 254-424 nautical miles and voyage time of about 21-36 hrs as also the attendant operating costs. The channel will become a valuable asset from national defence and security point of view enabling easier and quicker access between the coasts.

Due to the construction of infrastructure in the island, the land access, now available to the local fisher folk to Dhanushkody area for traditional fishing will be hindered unless alternative arrangements are made. The dredging and shipping operations will have to be so regulated as to cause minimum disturbance to the normal fishing activities.

The project will provide employment opportunities and avenues of additional income through establishment of small ancillary industries. The project will also trigger development of coastal trade between the ports south and north of Rameswaram consequently reducing the load and congestion on railways and roadways.

The project will help in saving considerable foreign exchange through reduction in oil import bill and generate revenue income from dues levied on ships transiting the channel which will add to the national economy.

ENVIRONMENTAL MANAGEMENT PLAN

Construction Phase

- No dredging will be done in Gulf of Mannar except in Adam's Bridge area
- Alignment of navigation route at Adam's Bridge in Gulf of Mannar will be minimum 20 km away from marine national park
- Land acquired for mobilization and monitoring of activity will be returned to users after completion of dredging activity
- A proper rehabilitation plan for the fisherman at Dhanushkody will be drawn during construction phase
- Dredged spoil comprising clay and sand upto 2 m of dredging depth will be used for reclaiming degraded land in Pamban island subject to approval of FED for CRZ. Balance dredged spoil will be disposed in sea at a depth 30-40 m, 20-25 km away from islands in National Marine Park in Gulf of Mannar. Dredged spoil generated in Palk Strait / Palk Bay area will be disposed in open sea in Bay of Bengal at 25-40 m depth, 30-60 km away from dredging area

- Safe distance (about 4 km) from international medial line will be maintained
- During dredging activities, the equipments, vessels, barges required for dredging and transportation of dredged spoil will be maintained in secured area and spillage of oil or any toxic material including paints, anticorrosive agents etc. will not be allowed to spill in sea/coastal waters
- Movement of barges for transporting dredged spoil to land area will not interfere with movement of fishing boats in both Gulf of Mannar and Palk Bay region adjoining the Adam's Bridge
- It is also recommended that existing jetties at Rameswaram which only cater to fishing activities presently should be augmented to cater to the requirement of handling dredging activities in Adam Bridge and Palk Bay area
- Transportation of heavy machinery and construction material in the vicinity of Adam's Bridge will be by sea route using the available navigational depths
- During transportation of heavy equipments and machinery by road, care will be taken to avoid traffic hazard, traffic congestion and if required roads will be augmented to meet the conditions of hazard free transportation.

Operational Phase

- All the ships originating from Tutitcorin Port will comply to International Maritime Standards and follow MARPOL convention (MARPOL 73/78)
- Discharge of bilge, ballast, treated sewage, solid wastes, oily wastes and spillage of cargo will not be allowed in the Gulf of Mannar and Palk Bay area
- The traffic of crude oil tankers will be allowed in this route with strict vigilance so as to avoid any possibilities of spillage in this region
- It will be ensured that ships navigating in this region should not use such paints and anticorrosive agents on ship bottom which can cause damage to marine organisms
- A pilot should be trained or environmental watcher will board the ship to watch marine animals viz. turtle, dolphins, sea cow etc. in the region and navigate the ship safely avoiding any damage to this fauna.
- It will be ensured that all the ships berthing at TPT as well as all those using the route without touching TPT will have proper treatment facilities for sewage however discharge of treated sewage will not be permitted in GOM and Palk Bay/Palk strait area
- Ships bypassing TPT and transiting the channel will be inspected for its navigational safety measures before it is allowed to enter proposed navigation route
- An oil spill contingency plan will be drawn by Tuticorin Port Trust with preparedness to prevent spread of spillage in Gulf of Mannar and Palk Bay area and its immediate recovery by deploying equipments and ships

- To benefit large fishing communities in the coastal area of Ramnathpuram and Rameshwaram, a corridor both in terms of space and time be provided to fisherman to use the channel in Adam's Bridge area for moving across Palk Bay to GOM and vice versa for fishing activity
- The jetties at Rameswaram are in dilapidated conditions. A programme to construct a few Jetties at Pamban island to augment fishing activity in the region be supported by TPT
- The traffic of ships carrying crude oil will be handled with strict vigilance so as to avoid possibility of spillage
- The oil spill contingency plan in operation at TPT will be extended to navigation activities in new channel
- A pilot will board the vessel either from Rameswaram or appropriate place to navigate ship through GOM area up to Bengal Channel in Palk Bay
- The channel will be properly marked by navigational light buoys
- Accidents by collision of ships with fishing boats will be totally prevented by slowing down the cruise speed and also alerting the fisherman by cautionary measures. During implementation and operational phases of the project, TPT will take action to avoid the collisions of ships with fishing boats or damage to fishing nets with cooperation from fishing communities, Navy, Coast Guards and other Govt. authorities
- Suitable timings apart from ship transit will be given for fishermen to continue with their fishing activities
- Maintenance dredging of about 0.55 million m^3 per year is envisaged in the channel based on data available for sediment transport across Palk Bay and Gulf of Mannar
- The dredged material will be mostly silt and clay and will not be disposed in sea. Instead it will be used to reclaim degraded areas on Pamban island, Ramnad and Mandapam coastal stretches
- To cater to increase in trade envisaged due to this project and to transfer benefit to local fisherman, a minor port facility can be created at Rameswaram in consultation with state authorities.

Annexure 4

Ram's bridge in man-made row—
Scientist find triggers claim that islet
chain was built by monkeys

M.R. Venkatesh

Chennai, May 7: Government scientists have suggested that an islet chain in the Palk Strait is man-made, triggering claims that it is the remnant of the bridge Ram's mythological monkey army built to Lanka.

The issue has raised political passions because a Rs. 2,427 crore navigation project that will save the country Rs. 1,000 crore a year requires the demolition of the ridge.

Adam's Bridge, a series of sand-dune islets and shallows south-east of Dhanshkodi near Rameshwaram, links India with Talaimannar off the Sri Lankan coast. It has long been held locally to be the bridge Ram built to invade Lanka and rescue Sita, and is called "Ramar Setu".

The Centre's department of earth sciences has given an "opinion" to the government that the islets are probably a result of human activity.

The department, under the ministry of science and technology, says the sand dunes have a base of coral and sandstone that seem to have been "transported" from elsewhere.

Its unpublished report, of which *The Telegraph* has a copy, says the naturally formed corals in Lakshadweep, the Andamans or the nearby Gulf of Mannar grow vertically from a hard-rock base. But the Adam's Bridge coral doesn't grow vertically and appears to "rest" loosely on the seabed.'

"The coral formations hardly occur 1 m to 2.5 m in length and rest on loose marine sands. Most... seem to be rounded pebbles of corals. These things appear to point that these...have been transported and placed in these areas," the department's note says.

"Since the calcareous sand stones and corals are less dense (and therefore lighter) than the normal hard rock and quite compact, probably these were used by (the) ancients to form a connecting link to Sri Lanka on the higher elevations of the Adam's Bridge ridge and this is analogous to (a) modern-day causeway."

The leaked report led to a ruckus in the Tamil Nadu Assembly on Friday. The Opposition, including the BJP, demanded that the ridge be spared and chief minister M. Karunanidhi hit back with accusations of a "north Indian" and "fundamentalist" plot to derail the project.

The Sethusamudram Ship Canal Project involves dredging the islets to deepen the Palk Strait and thus open a direct channel between India's west and east costs. Currently, ships have to make a detour around Sri Lanka.

The 167-km channel, dubbed the "Suez of the East", will shorten shipping routes by up to 424 nautical miles (780 km) and sailing time by 30 hours, saving fuel. India's import-export trade will save the Rs. 1,000 crore a year it now spends in foreign ex change because of transshipment of cargo outside the country, through Colombo.

The Opposition ADMK, BJP and the Janata Party cited the "scientific opinion" to buttress their case that the project, for which dredging is under way, should find an alternative route.

"Suddenly, some communal elements have banded together to give this controversy a religious hue, attempting to create a bloodbath here, just as they did by demolishing the Babri Masjid in Ayodhya to build a temple to Ram, "Karunanidhi told the House. "Most of these people opposing the project are north Indian religious fundamentalists."

ADMK chief Jayalalithaa has threatened to move court to stay the project if Adam's Bridge is touched. The ridge, which she wants spared in deference to "people's religious sentiments", acted as a barrier during the 2004 tsunami, protecting large parts of southern Tamil Nadu and Kerala.

Annexure 5

No. J-16011/6/99-IA-III
Government of India
Ministry of Environment & Forests

Paryavaran Bhavan,
CGO Complex,
Lodhi Road, New Delhi- 110003
8th April 1999

To
Shri S. Gopalan,
Development Adviser (Ports),
Ministry of Surface Transport,
Pariavahan Bhavan,
Parliament Street, New Delhi
FAX No. 3710836

Sub: Sethusamudram Ship Canal Project – reg.

Sir

1. I am directed to refer to your D.O. No. DW/DTM-4/97 dated 11th January 1999 on the above subject enclosing a copy of the Initial Environmental Examination made by the National Environmental Engineering Research Institute and subsequently presented to the officers of the Ministry on 24th March 1999.

2. Prima facie, the Ministry is not in favour of this Project as this Project has serious environmental implications with respect to marine park and the biosphere reserve located in that area. Since movement of oil tankers is also envisaged on the proposed ship canal, the possibility of oil pollution from accidental spills and disastrous consequences thereof to the sensitive eco-systems present in the marine national park and biosphere reserve can't be ruled out.

3. Your Ministry has sought our comments can the initial Environmental Report prepared by the NEERI. These are enclosed. This Ministry is of the strong opinion that from the environmental angle this Project should not be taken up at all.

Yours faithfully
Sd/-
(R. Anandakumar)
Director
Ph. 4364592

Annexure 6

From "Subramanian Swamy" ilky@sify.com
To   jsc-earthweb@mail.nasa.gov
Sent   Sunday, July 29, 2007 5:56 AM

Dear Sir,

I am seeking confirmation of whether you have very recently corresponded with a functionary of the Sethusamundram Canal Project of Government of India, regarding the Rama Setu otherwise known abroad as the Adam's Bridge, a causeway like formation between India and Sri Lanka, and whether Earthweb is a department of NASA as the claimed by the Project head at a press conference yesterday. I shall be much obliged for an early reply, because it has been claimed by the Project head that "Earthweb of NASA has concluded beyond reasonable doubt" that the so-called Adam's Bridge is a natural formation of coral rocks on site. Any documentation in this regard will be gratefully received.

Subramanian Swamy Ph.D. [Harvard]

Presently teaching at Harvard University [Summer term]

swamy@post.harvard.edu

Text of the E-mail Reply from NASA

Thank you for contacting us regarding this issue. Earthweb is a service e provided by the Image Science & Analysis Laboratory at the N ASA Johnson Space Center.

Our response to inquiries regarding Adam's Bridge is based solely on the information captured in the astronaut photography dataset. Astronaut photography does not provide information on the age of islands in the Palk Strait, nor can it provide information on the subsurface structure or composition of the islands. We therefore cannot speculate on the validity, or invalidity, of other origin narratives for the Palk Strait islands.

Chains of islands typically form from a variety of natural geological processes and their occurrence, by themselves, is not evidence of any human activity. We offer no conclusion regarding the ultimate origin of the Palk Strait islands in the response that has been widely quoted, we simply state that island chains form by natural processes. Modern geological though regarding island chains around d the world suggests that this statement is valid.

To interpret our response as a scientifically rigorous conclusion as to the nature of the Palk Strait islands is both a misinterpretation and misreporting, and is inappropriate considering the limitation of our data. To reach any such conclusion, detailed surface and subsurface geological and perhaps, anthropological information for the islands would need to be collected, analyzed, and published.

Thank you for your interest in astronaut photography of Earth!
Earthweb
The Gateway of Astronaut Photography of Earth
NASA Johnson Space Center
http://eol.jsc.nasa.gov

Statement of Dr. Subramanian Swamy

I demand the sacking of the Chairman of the Sethusamudram Canal Project, Mr. Raghupathy for ship blant lie at press conference on July 27th, wherein he claimed that the NASA had communicated to him that Rama Setu, called by toadies of British Imperialists as "Adam's Bridge", is a natural formation, and he was debunking the Hindu belief that it was built on the direction of Bhagwan Sri Rama.

In response to my e-mail query, the NASA has replied that it made no such communication [e-mails]xxx. The agency has clarified to me that "We therefore cannot speculate on the validity, or invalidity, of other narratives for the Palk Strait islands", thus denying the claim of the Chairman of the SSCP. The NASA censures those who "interpret our response [meaning the Chairman of SSCP] as a scientifically rigorous conclusion as to the nature of the Palk Strait islands is both a misrepresentation and misreporting, an inappropriate considering the limitations of our data."

Annexure 7

Dr. S.R. Rao
To
The Hon'ble Minister for Shipping and Transport
Government of India
New Delhi

Sub : Preventing damage to the ancient Ram-Sethu (Adam's Bridge) and declaring it as "UNDERWATER WORLD HERITAGE" site under the UNESCO CONVENTION.

Sir,

I, as President of the Society, for Marine Archeology. National Institute of Oceanography, Goa, and also as a former elected member of the UNESCO-sponsored ICOMOS International Committee for Underwater Cultural Heritage, earnestly request you kindly to save the traditionally known Ram-Sethu mentioned in various Puranas, as a bridge built by the legendary Hero of Ramayana. This natural rock connecting the Mannar island with Rameswaram island is now submerged in the sea owing to the rise in the sea level during the least 4000 years or more but it was perhaps in the intertidal zone and not unlikely to have been further raised by piling up of rubble to enable Rama's followers to reach Lanka. Hence it is of great emotional value as a sacred tirtha. But as a marine archaeologist, I feel it is of great historical importance too. We found at Dwarka natural rock was dressed suitably as a wharf for berthing ships about 3600 years ago. Similarly rock (Adam's Bridge) connecting Mannar and Rameswaram must have been used by piling up rubble manually on it to enable the Vanaras to reach Lanka. For the ancient marine engineers who could build a tidal dock at Lothal in 2300 B.C. and modify a ridge for berthing ships at Dwarka, the piling up of stones on the so called Adam's bridge for an army to reach Lanka was on easy task. Hence both from marine archaeological an traditional points of view Rama Sethu deserves to be decalred as an UNDERWATER WORLD HERITAGE SITE. I cite below the archaeological an technological criteria for recommending Rama-Sethu to be World Heritage site are as per the annexure 1 (p. 77 of the journal of Marine Archaeology 1997-98 published by marine Archaeology Society – Copy enclosed), which includes structures of archeological as well as memorial significance.

Sir, I would request you kindly to see that the cutting of the rock or any kind of damage to the rock is avoided. It is no less important that Swami Vivekananda

Rock where a memorial is built. Alternate routes suggested by experts (vide Route 4 in Fig. 1 enclosed) may kindly be considered in the interest of saving the Underwater Cultural Heritage of India namely Rama Sethu or Adam's Bridge. My study of the submergence of Poomphar shows that most of the ancient sites on east coast are being swallowed by the sea. The latest victim is the shore temple at Tarangambadi.

During my two visit to Sri Lanka, as a member of the ICUCH I visited the Ram Sethu site and had discussions with Commander Devendra Somasiri, another member of ICUCH from Sri Lanka about its importance as a Heritage site.

With highest regards,

Yours sincerely

Sd/-

Dr. S.R. Rao

President, Society for Marine Archaeology (GOA)

Copy to: Sh. S. Kalyanraman

Annexure 8

JANATA PARTY

A-77, Nizamuddin (East) New Delhi – 110 013
Phone : 24353805 Fax : 24357388
Mobile : 9810194279
Website : www.janataparty.org
E-mail : swamy@post.harvard.edu

October 5, 2007
Ms. Ambika Soni
Minister of Culture
Transport Bhavan,
New Delhi

Dear Ms. Soni

I write to draw your attention to the ill-fated Counter Affidavit filed by your Ministry in reply to my Affidavit praying for recognition of the Rama Setu as an ancient monument under the Ancient Monuments and Archaeological Sites Act, (1958). In that Couter Affidavit your Ministry has stated that there was no scientific study to show that Rama Setu was a construction. This, however, appears to be quite untrue because according to a report prepare under the direction of Dr. S. Badrinarayan, now retired Director of Geological survey of India and also formerly coordinator Survey Division of the National Institute of Ocean Technology (NIOT), Ministry of Earth Science, titled "Report on the Geological and Geotechnical assessment of the subsea strata for the proposed Sethusamudram Channel Project (Doc No. NIOT/C-1046/ETT-Sethu-VBC-B4 dated 14th February, 2005, the Rama Setu is a structure in which the coral rocks in the structure appear to have been brought there and placed and not naturally evolved at the site. Hence this hoary structure is a constructed one and since clearly over a hundred years old, entitled to be considered to be recognized as an ancient monument. I therefore write again to you to urge you to order a proper investigation into the origin of the Rama Setu and take necessary steps to have it declared as a ancient monument. It would be proper for me to inform you that this letter would be placed as part of my supplementary Affidavit along with your reply, if any.

Yours sincerely,

Sd/-

(Subramanian Swamy)

Annexure 9
Non-Declaration of Ram Setu as National Monument

RAJYA SABHA

Minister for Tourism and Culture Smt. Ambika Soni has said that no such directions have been received from the Madras High Court to declare Ram Setu (between India and Sri Lanka) as national monument under the National Monument and Archaeological Place Law, 1958.

In a written reply in the Rajya Sabha today she said, no archaeological study has been made in respect of Ram Setu by the Archaeological Survey of India by the Archaeological Survey of India.

As per the scientific evidence available so far, Ram Setu does not fulfill the criteria to be declared as a monument of national importance under the provisions of the Ancient Monuments and Archaeological Sites and Remains Act, 1958.

Annexure 10
Sethu plan tweak can lower tsunami risk

By Abhishek Shuklain Visakhapatnam

Tsunami risk to the south Kerala coast would increase once the Sethusamudram canal becomes a reality, tsunami expert Tad S. Murthy said at the Indian Science Congress in Visakhapatnam.

This threat, however, can be mitigated if the entry to the canal from the Bay of Bengal side can be slightly tilted towards north, says Murthy. he current design of the canal could funnel the energy of tsunami waves towards the south Kerala coast causing large-scale devastation, said the expert.

Murthy said he had conveyed his concerns to N.K. Raghupathy, former head of Tuticorin Port Trust, way back in 2005. But the project authorities have rejected his advice.

The Sethusamudram Corporation says, "The entry of tsunami into the channel will be dissipated by Adams Bridge and later absorbed by the Gulf of Mannar. Therefore, the apprehension of devastation in southern Kerala is not realistic." The corporation claims that results of several hydrodynamic modeling studies suggest that increase in magnitude of the sea caused by the tsunami will be along Adams Bridge, thus avoiding any change in its current status.

When asked about the role of Adams Bridge in preventing tsunami devastation in coastal areas, Murthy said such formations affected the flow of tsunami waves but the extent of the impact needs to be studied.

He suggested that computer modeling studies be undertaken to assess the likely impact of these formations on the coastline. "If we place any object in the normal flow of water it will affect the flow and redistribution of the energies but how that happens needs to be studied," he said.

Meanwhile, the Indian Space Research Organisation (ISRO) officials said the space institute was lining the Kerala coast with automated warning systems that would update information every 15 minutes. At present, the update is done every six hours, which misses out on weather phenomenon of shorter durations called meso scale storm surges. These surges, although small, flood coastal areas and disturb normal lives of the locals.

The space agency has successfully installed 64 automated systems on the coasts of Kerala. The agency plans to take their number to 300 across India. The information from these stations is now sent to the meteorological department in Kerala but once fully functional, the information will be sent to the Indian Institute of Tropical Meteorology in Pune.

Annexure 11

Impact on Tsunami on Sethusamudram Shipping Channel and the neighbouring coastal areas

INTERVIEW WITH PROFESSOR TAD S. MURTHY

Prof. Tad S. Murthy is one of the most respected Tsunami Experts around the world; he advises the Government of Canada on Tsunamis and had played an important role in the development of the *'Baird' simulation model of the December 26th Tsunami*. He was in the Editorial Board of the most prestigious Tsunami Journal *"Science of Tsunami Hazards"* for many years.

He along with Dr. Arun Bapat, had analysed the *Tsunamis of the Indian Ocean in 1999.**

He was in India this January to participate in the *'Brainstorming' Session on the Tsunami* of 26th December organized jointly by Department of Science & Technology (DST), Department of Ocean Development (DOD), Council of Scientific and Industrial Research (CSIR) and Indian National Science Academy (INSA) on 21-22 January, 2005 at New Delhi. Subsequently, when National Institute of Oceanography, Goa organised a *National Workshop on Formulation of Science Plan for "Coastal Hazard Preparedness"* on 18-19 February 2005, he set the tone for the workshop with his paper titled "Perspectives on Coastal Hazard Preparedness".

The following is an e-mail interview conducted with him by the Editor of this web portal on 7-11 July 2005.

The interview assumes its importance following the *July 24, 2005 Nicobar 7.3 R Earthquake* that had *caused much panic*. It also assumes its importance as the *Expert Level discussion between India and Sri Lanka* on the possible impact of the Sethusamudram Shipping Channel Project on the marine and coastal environments of both the countries is scheduled on 1 August 2005 at New Delhi.

* ["Tsunamis on the coastlines of India" *Science of Tsunami Hazards Volume 17(3), 1999]*

Question: Respected Professor! Would you please tell me what you personally think about the reply given to the Prime Minister by Tuticorin Port Trust with regard to your critical opinion about the present alignment of the Sethusamudram Shipping Channel published in the *Indian Express* dated 18 February 2005?

Prof. Tad S. Murthy: I would first of all share with you a bit of background on my slight involvement with Sethusamudram Shipping Channel Project.

In January 2005, I was in India as the tsunami expert on the delegation of Prime Minister Paul Martin (Canada) visit to various Asian countries following the tsunami. On 18th January I was with the prime minister at a press briefing in Delhi.

Later some *Indian Express* and *Telegraph* reporters spoke to me about SSCP and I made these comments. Earlier I was working on a paper on SSCP and was interested in the scientific aspects of the project.

In May Tuticorin Port Trust (TPT) sent me a fax dated early February asking for my comments and said that the project is finalized by end of Feb and they wanted my comments within 24 hours. I replied to Mr. Raghunadh (IAS officer) (read : Mr. Raghupathy – Editor) that I received his fax only in May and possibly I cannot reply by mid-Feb. I sent a page explaining why the eastern entrance of the channel should be re-oriented.

After a few days I received a reply saying that his experts outright dismissed my idea as ridiculous and has absolutely no merit. I did not do anything after this, as I have no official involvement. If you include my student days in the Andhra University and later at the university of Chicago, I have more than 45 years of experience with tsunamis worldwide and I know what I am talking about.

I cannot understand why Tuticorin Port Trust could not find me when everyone else can find me. The *Indian Express* newspaper article clearly says that I was staying at the Taj Palace Hotel in Delhi and will be there for another week or so.

Question: How do you react to *Tuticorin Port Trust's statement* that the suggestion you had made with respect to the present alignment of the Channel and its possible chance of acting as a conduit to future tsunamis, thus paving way to causing damage to South Kerala coast as untenable?

Prof. Tad S. Murthy: Tuticorin Port Trust (TPT) of course can draw whatever conclusions they want to.

I feel that the Bay of Bengal entrance of the present orientation of the channel will undoubtedly funnel tsunami energy into the channel and this will meet the tsunami traveling from South of Sri Lanka at the southern part of Kerala and through constructive interference will augment the tsunami wave amplitudes. The southern part of Kerala was not much impacted by the 26th December 2004 tsunami mainly because the tsunami that arrived from the Indian Ocean has to diffract around Sri Lanka, which necessarily has to take a very wide turn (because tsunamis are long gravity waves and cannot bend as easily as short waves, just like a big car versus a mini. A mini cut cut corners, but a big car has to take very wide turns.) and missed south Kerala.

It is very easy to show that SSCP channel with a depth of 12m will indeed provide another route for the tsunami and the energy will be directed towards south Kerala.

I have no official connection with the SSCP, only scientific curiosity plus my concern that South Kerala will be put at risk in future. I donot worry that TPT does not think much of my ideas or me. I do not have to justify myself to TPT. I have to fight my battles, not with TPT but in the field of peer reviewed international scientific journals.

To summarize, a re-orientation of the eastern entrance of the channel towards northwest will fix the tsunami problem.

Why this concerns me is a parallel example in the Alberni canal on Vancouver Island, British Columbia province of Canada. In the March 2uth 1964 Alaska earthquake tsunami, outside of Alaska, the largest tsunami amplitude was at the head of the Alberni canal well inland and not at the open coast as everyone expected. Later when I joined the Canadian Oceanographic Service, *I explained this* as due to quarter wave resonance amplification.

The SSP canal has many characteristics similar to the Alberni canal, and this is the reason I am concerned.

Question: Professor! The Detailed Project Report prepared by L & T – Ramboll has finalized *the location of the dumping sites for the dredged materials.*

They are located in Bay of Bengal and Gulf of Mannar and have a depth ranging from 30 to 40 km. These sites happen to lie just north of and south of the entrance and exist of the channel. What are the chances for these sites to remain safe and stable during the time of a future tsunamis and cyclones? Also, what are the chances for them to be carried over into the channel in the event of future tsunamis and cyclones?

Prof. Tad S. Murthy: I need to do some back of the envelope calculations to precisely answer your question, which I will do in a few days.

However, my initial intuition is that the dumping sites will not be completely stable, especially if they happen to be in *the path of the tsunami waves.* They may be relatively stable from the cyclones and storm surges, since these do not cause much bottom scouring like tsunamis. The safety issue arises if they are contaminants, especially radioactive contaminants.

Again, I need to do a back of the envelope type computation for a definite answer, again my intuition is that the cyclone and storm surge effects will be less as compared to tsunamis. Certainly tsunamis have the potential to pull all this material back into the channel, if the orientation is right.

The basic question I will attempt to answer through an analytical analysis is simply this.

Would storm surges and tsunamis have the energy to move the dredged material back into the channel? As I said earlier, my present feeling is, storm surges probably will not move much material, but tsunamis definitely would. I will try to quantify this in a couple of days.

As per the TPT's conclusion that not re-orientation of the eastern entrance of the channel is required, I absolutely disagree with it. I do not need to analyze that any more.

I have analyzed the problem to my complete satisfaction.

I now have more definite answers to your questions.

Inspite of what the TPT says, there is a real threat to southern Kerala from future tsunamis from SSP.

At this time I do not have the resources to actually do a numerical model to determine the quantitative aspects of the movement aspects of the dredged material.

(However) I did some analytical analysis of whether cyclones (and storm surges) and tsunamis can move the dredged material from Palk Bay into the channel.

The impact from cyclones and storm surges will be minimal, but tsunamis can move a significant amount of the dredged material into the channel.

1 August 2005

Prof. Murty reiterated his concerns in February 2007. From Personal Communication, Feb. 2007: "I requested him (Raghupathy) to consider slightly re-orienting the entrance of the Sethu canal on the Bay of Bengal side, so that in future tsunami events, tsunami energy will not be preferentially funneled into the Setu canal. Shri Raghupathy assured me that he will look into this matter. When a senior IAS officer like Shri Raghupathy says something, I believe him and I have no further concerns on this matter."

URL is an animated model of how the last tsunami moved, doing a paradkshinam around the Ramar bridge:

This shows the spread of the massive displacement of waters displaced by the plate tectonic event at Aceh. The spread was dosn the southern Tamilnadu coastline, circled the entire Srilanka island and moved partially into Kerala and towards the Ramar Bridge. This circling around Srilanka occurred because the Ramar bridge acted as a natural shoal barrier preventing the inflow of waters.

If a Setusamudram channel is dug through the bridge, it will act as the channel for the waters to flow directly into the entire southern bharatam coastline beyond Dhanushkodi and into the coastline of Kerala right into the Konkan region. The devastation of such direct onrush of tsunami waters will be incalculable.

There are clear indications that the environmental clearance was done without taking into account fundamental engineering and cost- benefit factors:

1. Effect of a tsunami-type of event on the project (all scientists are unanimous that a recurrence of tsunami's cannot be ruled out).
2. Locations for dumping the dredged sand.
3. Costs of continuous dredging given the continuous sea currents which tend to create the shoals and again rebuild the Ramar bridge making the project inoperateable for most of the time.

4. The types of naval craft which can navigate through the project channel (Apparently, the heavy oil tankers cannot go through this channel given the limited draft and will continue to circumnavigate around Srilanka and through Straits of Malacca to reach the markets of Southeast and East Asia.) There has been no market study of the numbers and types of vessels which will navigate through the channel and the freight rates expected to be paid by these vessel for being tugged through the channel.

In the interests of safety of the lives of the coastal people, it is prudent to stop the project work until the fundamental factors are re-studied and re-evaluated. It is also essential to involve NIOT and create a Marine Archaeological Unit to study the archaeology of the Ramar Bridge and Kizhakkarai (Tiruchendur) where a s'ankha industry flourishes. It will be a tragedy of incalculable proportion to the cultural tradition of Bharatam, if this industry were to be devastated by the project. It will be prudent to study the impact of the project on the cultural aspirations of the people and industries such as the ones which support livelihood of s'ankha divers. Impact on fisheries and future projects for desalination of seawater to provide drinking water to coastal towns should also be evaluated. The possibility of choosing an alternative route for the channel with little impact on the Ramar bridge should also be re-studied, taking into account the satellite image analyses which sow that the secular historical trend of incursions and recessions of seaters from almost the entire Bharatam coastline from Drarka through Gulf of Khambat, through Gulf of Mannar upto Ganga Sagar (West Bengal)—caused by a number of factors not excluding plate tectonics and global warming cycles. The received narratives of the submergence of Kumarikandam should be a pointer to the imperative of careful studies before embarking on projects which hurt the cultural sentiments of the people who are inheritors of a glorious sea-faring, maritime, riverine civilization continuum.

Annexure 12

'Adam's Bridge a man-made structure'

July 31, 2007

In our series on Ram Sethu and the Sethusamudram Canal project, we had earlier interviewed world-renowned tsunami expert Dr Tad S Murthy and Dr Kalyanaraman, a researcher on the subject.

This time, we discuss the feasibility of the project with Geologist Dr. Badrinarayanan.

Dr Badrinarayanan was former director of the Geological Survey of India. He was also former coordinator of the survey division of the National Institute of Ocean Technology, Ministry of Earth Science, in Chennai.

As a geologist who has done studies on the geological aspects of the area where Sethu Samudram Canal Project is being undertaken, Dr. Badrinarayanan puts forth some interesting findings on the area in an interview to Shobha Warrier.

As a geologist, how do you describe Ram Sethu? Is it a man-made structure or natural formation?

It is not a natural formation; the top portion of it appears to be a man-made structure. To understand what I am saying from the geological point of view, you have to get to know several things.

What is known as Adam's Bridge is originally a natural grade divide separating the Bay of Bengal and the Indian Ocean to the south. So, the geological aspects are different on either side.

About 18,000 years ago, we have Ice age when the sea level was lower by 130 metres than what it is now. Due to de-glaciation, the sea level rose.

Around 7,300 years back, there was major flooding and the sea level rose to 4 metres more than what it is today. This has been verified by several researchers throughout the world. But the bridge that connects India and Sri Lanka is different; it is not just a sand dune.

Have studies been done on this particular phenomenon?

We (Geological Survey of India) were asked to carry out surveys for locating the Sethu Samudram Canal project by the project authorities in 2004-05.

Any Startling Revelations?

When we reached near Adam's Bridge, there was sudden rise in the land level. From about 10-12 metre, it rose one metre to half a metre. So our vessel could not go and survey the area. In some areas, we did survey using small boats.

The northern side of Adam's Bridge is the rough Palk Bay, which is prone to periodic cyclonic storms, and the tranquil southern side in the Gulf of Mannar, which is unpolluted and pristine.

Corals grew in the tranquil Gulf of Mannar but not in the turbulent Palk Bay as they grow only in tranquil waters. There are about 21 islands full of corals in the Gulf of Mannar side but not even a single coral on the northern side of Adam's Bridge.

I would say no proper geological survey was done in the area. Normally before any major engineering project, GSI conducts engineering geological study, geological study, geo tectonic study, seismic study, etc. so that we will know whether the project is safe or not.

You Mean No Such Studies Were Done Before This Project?

Earlier, GSI had done some drilling but only at the deeper level of about 180-200 metres, but they have not mentioned anything about what was happening at the top portion.

We did a study from NIOT on our own connecting between Rameswaram and the international waters. We did around 10 bore holes along the Adam's Bridge alignment. Four of the bore holes were along the islands (where sands go on shifting) and six in the water.

Everywhere, after top 6 metres, we found marine sands on top and below that was a mixed assemblage of corals, calcareous sand stones, and boulder like materials. Surprisingly below that up to 4-5 metres, again we found loose sand and after that, hard formations were there.

How Do You Explain the Presence of Loose Sand?

It shows the structure is not natural. I will explain. Corals are found only on rocks and such hard surfaces. Here, below the corals and boulders, we are getting loose sand, which means it is not natural.

And, on top of the loose sand, which was formed when the sea level was low, our divers found boulders. Boulders normally occur on land and they are a typical riverine character.

DOES THAT MEAN THE BOULDERS WERE BROUGHT THERE FROM SOMEWHERE?

That is exactly what I am saying. The boulders are not in-situ. They are not a marine local formation. We feel somebody dumped the boulders to use it as a causeway. The boulders on tope of the loose sand are transported to that place. As they are found above loose sand, it is quite obvious that they were brought and dumped there by somebody.

HOW OLD WERE THE BOULDERS?

I told you earlier that 7,300 years ago, sea level was 4 metres above what it is today. In Rameswaram, Pamban, Tuticorin, etc, we see old corals on the land, and they are not raised by any geological process. It happened because sea level was higher (at the time they were formed). We did dating on them and found that they are 7,300 years old.

From 7,300 to 5,800 years ago, the sea level was high. From 5,800 to 5,400 years ago, the sea level was low. Again, from 5,400 to 4,000, the sea level was higher by 2 metres than what it is today. That is why we are getting two sets of corals at two levels. Dr PK Banerji has carried out a lot of studies on the raised corals and his papers have appeared in reputed international scientific journals. His arguments are backed by very good scientific data.

So, either between 5,800 to 5,400 years ago, or (some time since) 4,000 years ago, somebody appeared to have brought all the boulders and dumped them there. All the aerial pictures show that Adam's Bridge is 2 to 3 kilometres wide. On the eastern side, it is high. So, anyone could take advantage of the raised portion and must have dumped these boulders so that he could cross the bridge.

HOW DO THE BOULDERS LOOK, AND FROM WHAT WERE THEY MADE?

The shape of the boulders and the type of material clearly indicate that this is a man-made structure. We saw similar rocks on Rameswaram islands and also in Pamban. On either side of the railway bridge, you can see these formations as well as the raised corals. There are indications of quarrying also there.

All these things lead us to believe that 2 to 2.5 metres of packed rubble or material appears to be a modern day causeway. For 30 km, nobody dumbs materials like that. Obviously, it was dumped to use it to cross the sea. Moreover, they are compact and light.

It is also quite obvious that the boulders were used to cross over because in all the bore holes we made in the entire stretch of Adam's Bridge, we saw the same material. It appears like a rock-filled structure.

If it is a geological phenomenon, you will find the oldest formation below and the newer ones on top. I would rather call it an anthropogenic (pertaining to the effect of human beings on the natural world) causeway rather than a bridge.

WHAT ELSE HAVE YOU LEARNT FROM THE STUDIES YOU HAVE CONDUCTED ALONG RAM SETHU?

We have found that geologically and geotectonically, this area is very sensitive. Many people are not aware of it. All around the north, there are spots where there is very high temperature below. When we drilled, we encountered hot sprints of 60 to 70 degrees Celsius.

Whenever there are earthquakes in Sri Lanka, we get the vibrations in the Indian side also. That means a major fault is running there and it is very sensitive. This area is also known to have earthquakes and they had happened one or two centuries back. To the north and the south, there are indications of old volcanoes.

BECAUSE OF THESE HOT SPRINTS AND PRESENCE OF VOLCANIC ZONES, DO YOU FEEL IF DISTURBED, IT WILL AFFECT THE EQUILIBRIUM OF THE ENTIRE AREA?

What you said is correct. That is why, before venturing into anything, you have to make a comprehensive study. This area has attained some sort of equilibrium over many centuries, and all the drilling and blasting of rocks may activate the fault and may trigger seismic activity or earthquakes.

It may also trigger other events, which may be very detrimental. That is because the hot water from the north, which is blocked by the Adam's Bridge, will come to the south and will disturb the coral islands. The result will be the destruction of the corals.

Not only that, whenever there is a major tsunami or cyclones in the Bay of Bengal, it is blocked by the so called bridge. Out of 18 depressions in the Bay of Bengal at least six turn into cyclones.

When we interviewed the tsunami expert Dr Tad S Murthy, he said if not for the bridge, the entire southern part of Kerala would have been affected badly.

Yes, it would have completely affected the entire south India. We were the people who suggested it. We had done a study, of course not knowing tsunami is coming, and felt the structure will prevent the Tuticorin area, the southern part of Kerala and all the coral islands from getting affected.

The calm tranquil water in the Gulf of Mannar full of coral islands is because it is protected all around. Why do you want to destroy it when nature has blessed you with something so beautiful? This is the first declared marine national park in the country.

Another point I want to make is, some dams trigger earth quakes. There is a possibility it can happen here also. So, it is prudent on part of the government to study all these aspects before taking a major decision.

Do you feel the construction of Sethu Samudram project was
initiated in a hurry without conducting proper study?

I think so. This portion is not like any sand dune. This is a very sensitive heat
flowing area. I feel the Geological Survey of India should be asked to do a survey.

Was the Geological Survey of India not asked to do a study
on this project?

No. Nobody has carried out any survey at all. We only did a survey to locate the
alignment. So, but what is needed is a comprehensive study.

What has been formed over centuries by nature cannot be disturbed. In foreign
countries, even a hundred-year-old structure is preserved and this looks like it is
thousands of years old. No doubt such a canal is essential but not at the cost of
nature. We are definitely for progress but our progress should be sustainable.

Annexure 13

Issues Raised During Public Hearing Meetings and Response of Project Authorities

Issues Raised in Public Hearings

1. This project will result in displacement of fishermen.
2. People at Arimunai and Dhanashkodi will be evacuated due to land acquisition for administrative buildings.
3. Fish breeding will be reduced due to this project.
4. While implementing the project fisherman should not be affected since the Kodaikarai and Muthukattai are the main fish breeding area. Fish production will be affected.
5. Livelihood and welfare of fishermen will be affected.
6. Welfare of the fishermen will be affected.
7. Dredging of channel will reduce the fishing area of Tamil Nadu Fishermen.
8. This project will implement time restriction which will affect the fishing activity.
9. Transfer of fish will occur due to ship movement.
11. Spillage of oil and plastic materials into the sea will affect the fish breeding.
12. Fisherman community will be wiped out due to pollution breeding.
13. Rare fish species sea cow, sea turtle and dolphins will be affected.
14. Non-availability of documents/reports by NEERI
15. Sedimentation will occur in the canal during monsoon leading to heavy loss to the Government.
16. During cyclone the channel will be unusable because of deposition of heavy silt.
17. The earlier alignment recommended by Screening Committee may be considered.
18. The project is note economically viable and sustainable.

19. The project will not be completed within 3 years definitely it will take 30 years.

20. This project will change the current pattern and that will have negative impact on fishing. Increase in Temperature. Increase in turbidity during construction will destruct fish species.

21. The mangroves will vanish due to implementation of this project. Dredging of channel will spoil mangroves in Muthupettai, Kodiyakarai and Athiramapattinam. Implementation of this project will destroy canal reef, algae sea breeds.

22. a. The dredged material will have an environment impact
    b. Disposal of dredged spoil in the sea will alter the level of dissolved oxygen.
    c. There will be environmental degradation.

23. Damage to fishing nets due to movement of ships

Issues: 1. This project will result in displacement of fishermen.

2. People at Arimunai and Dhanashkodi will be evacuated due to land acquisition for administrative buildings.

Response : The project envisages construction of shore facilities to cater to needs of the channel in Adam's Bridge area vis. Service jetties, slipways, buoys yard, repair workshop as also staff and administration buildings for facilitation regulated traffic in the vicinity of Adam's Bridge area. The locations of land-based structures and the extent of area required for their construction has been identified on Pamban Island (as suggested in the EIA report) in consultation with local authorities. Most of the land east of Rameswaram is barren and covered by sand and scant vegetation. There are few hamlets of Arimunai and Dhanushkodi who are engaged in fishing. These fishermen will be displaced only in the event of the land based facilities being planned in this area. However, in consultation with the District Authorities. Government land on which there is no inhabitation at present has only been identified for land based facilities. Utilization of the land for the purpose will be contingent upon CRZ clearances, not within the scope of the present application for environment clearance for the channel. Land on Pamban island was also identified in the EIA report for disposal of dredged materials. Utilization of the land for the purpose, subject to its availability, will also be contingent upon investment decision as land reclamation is a costlier option compared to sea disposal, and CRZ clearances, not within the scope of the present environment clearance for the channel. However, given that the canal will pass through Adam's Bridge area, the pressure on land based facilities would be negligible in comparison to that envisaged in earlier studies where land locked canal cutting through Pamban Island was proposed. (Refer EIA Report) Therefore, during the construction of the channel no dislocation of the fishermen is envisaged. For land based facilities which will be set up only after obtaining CRZ clearance in due course, the identification of land in such a way that it does not have any inhabitation, in consultation with district authorities, obviates the need for any displacement of fishermen.

Issues: 3. Fish breeding will be reduced due to this project.

4. While implementing the project fisherman should not be affected since the Kodaikarai and Muthukattai are the main fish breeding area. Fish production will be affected.

Response: The fish production grounds are mostly confined to coral reef area and margroves forest in the coastal area and around the islands. There is about 100 sq. kms. Of coral reef in the Gulf of Mannar and Palk Bay. The Coastal areas are also considered to be breeding grounds. This project does not envisage any disturbance to the breeding grounds viz., coral reefs, mangroves or the islands either during construction or during operation phase because of the stringent environment management plan such as –

(i) No disposal of dredged material in Palk Bay or near Marine National park in Gulf of Mannar.

(ii) No permission for disposal of any kind of wastes in the Gulf of Mannar/Palk Bay area. Hydrodynamic modeling was carried out to study the base line spatial tidal current distributions in the GoM and the Palk Bay and to estimate the changes that could be brought about due to the proposed channel. The Focus has been to predict the change in the direction and magnitude of the vector currents due to the change in bathymetry resulting from modeling. These studies carried out by NEERI for change in current pattern near Adam's bridge and adjacent locations in Palk Bay and Gulf of Mannar reveal that:-

(a) There will be no significant change in current directions and magnitude near coral reef areas, consequent to construction of the channel.

(b) The current direction will remain nearly the same after creation of the channel in Adam's Bridge area.

(c) Average current direction near the channel will remain parallel to the channel.

The current pattern in Palk Bay near the Pamban Island before creation of the channel is 270° - 340° i.e., towards north-west. This direction would not change in the near shore area. In the Palk Bay and Palk Strait area, the current will remain parallel to the channel and significant change in current direction and magnitude is not envisaged based on the earlier tracer studies conducted in this region.

The project envisages creation of a 300m wide channel, situated atleast 20km away from the nearest island, forming part of the National Marine Park. Even more distance has been maintained from other breeding centers where mangroves are situated. Any impact on the fish production grounds could be only on account of change in the direction and magnitude of the current near the production grounds in the after-channel-scenario or turbidity around them. The aforesaid studies would indicate that the channel will have no impact on the fish production grounds due to any such change in the current.

As regards turbidity, the dredged material will be disposed of 20-25km away from GoM Biosphere and, therefore, the EIA study does not envisage movement of the silt from the dumping ground towards the National Marine Park. An exercise using dispersion modeling was carried out to study impact of the dredged spoil on turbidity of sea water using CORMIX model. It has been inferred from the studies that the effect of the silty water when discharged will be localized and restricted to about 1500m from the discharge point. However, the plume will not surface immediately and the concentration of the suspended soil in sea water will return to normal after 1500m in the line of advection. The envisaged dredging activities in the area likely to cause much less turbidity than the international threshold, and thus the likely risk to marine biodata even in the vicinity of the dredging area is going to be minimal.

A potential source of pollution of the marine environment during the operation phase of the project relates to ship discharge – oily ballast, bilge water and sewage. The EMP has stipulated that during dredging activities, the equipments, vessels, barges, etc. will be maintained in secured area and spillage oil or any toxic material in sea/coastal waters will have to comply with MARPOL convection 1973/78 and CPCB restrictions for discharge of bilge, ballast, effluence's etc. into the sea. However, keeping in view the sensitivity of the region, ships will not be allowed to discharge any effluents into the sea.

The project envisages construction of shore facilities to cater to needs of the channel in Adam's Bridge area viz. service jetties, slipways, buoys yard, repair workshop as also staff and administration buildings for facilitation regulated traffic in the vicinity of Adam's Bridge area. The locations of land-based structures and the extent of area required for their construction has been identified on Pamban Island (as suggested in the EIA report) in consultation with local authorities. Most of the land east of Rameswaram is barren and covered by sand and scant vegetation. There are few hamlets of Arimunai and Dhanushkodi who are engaged in fishing. These fishermen will be displaced only in the event of the land based facilities being planned in this area. However, in consultation with the District Authorities, Government land on which there is no inhabitation at present has only been identified for land based facilities. Utilization of the land for the purpose will be contingent upon CRZ clearances, not within the scope of the present application for environment clearance for the channel. Land on Pamban island was also identified in the EIA report for disposal of dredged materials. Utilization of the land for the purpose, subject to its availability, will also be contingent upon investment decision as land reclamation is a costlier option compared to sea disposal, and CRZ clearances, not within the scope of the present environment clearance for the channel. However, given that the canal will pass through Adam's Bridge area, the pressure on land based facilities would be negligible in comparison to that envisaged in earlier studies where land locked canal cutting through Pamban Island was proposed. (Refer EIA Report) Therefore, during the construction of the channel no dislocation of the fishermen is envisaged. For land based facilities which will be set up only after obtaining CRZ clearance in due course, the identification of land in such a way that it does not have any inhabitation, in consultation with district authorities, obviates the need for any displacement of fishermen.

Issues: 5. Livelihood and welfare of fishermen will be affected.

6. Welfare of the fishermen will be affected.

7. Dredging of channel will reduce the fishing area of Tamil Nadu Fishermen.

8. This project will implement time restriction which will affect the fishing activity.

Response: As neither fish production grounds nor fishing activities will be affected due to the channel either in the construction or operation phase as already explained, the project rather than adversely affecting the socio-economic status of the fishermen, will upgrade their socio-economic status due to the following.

Fishermen will be able to freely transit through Adam's Bridge between Palk Bay and Gulf of Mannar, thereby enlarging the area of their fishing operations. (EIA report: Page 7.4).

There are rich resources of fish and shrimps in Palk Bay, Gulf of Mannar and the Indian Ocean and the Indian Ocean and at present the catches are being sent by means of refrigerated lorries to Kochi and Chennai for onward export to Japan and United States. Instead of this, the fishing harbour at Rameswaram can be upgraded into a Port from where the catches can be directly exported. This will promote maritime trade along the residents of the islands and ameliorate their present backwardness and conditions of distress for which the Government of the state and at the Center of ten invest in social grants for removal of such distress. This will also be an indirect benefit to the National exchequer.

(Techno-Economic Feasibility Report)

There will be significant direct employment generated in the project. TPT's experience has shown that there are several posts for which only fishermen's wards have the requisite qualification and, therefore, are recruited. Therefore, significant employment opportunities, direct and indirect could be available to the fishermen families, providing them an opportunity of changing over to other avenues of employment.

Issues: 9. Transfer of fish will occur due to ship movement.

Response : The channel will facilitate navigation of ships. At the same time it will facilitate the movement of fishes and other biota from the Bay of Bengal to the Indian Ocean and vice-versa. By this way, the entry of oceanic and alien species into the Palk Bay and the Gulf of Mannar, as also the dispersal of endemic species outside the Palk Bay and the Gulf of Mannar could occur.

(EIA Report)

Researchers have reported in their papers that such alien species is a continuing phenomenon. Many scientists and fishermen have expressed the view that entry of such alien species into Palk Bay through the dredged channel in Palk Bay could enrish the fish population.

Issues: 11. Spillage of oil and plastic materials into the sea will affect the fish breeding.

12. Fisherman community will be wiped out due to pollution breeding.

Response: The proposed alignment in the Gulf of Mannar is more than 20 kms away from the Islands constituting the National Marine Park in the Gulf of Mannar. Therefore, as explained already, the marine biological resources around these islands will not be affected to any significant level. The existing level of primary productivity in the project area will remain practically unaltered during the construction and operation phases of the channel. There would not be any significant change in water quality including turbidity due to the proposed deployment of cutter suction/trailer suction hopper dredgers for capital and maintenance dredging.

A potential source of pollution of the marine environment during the operation phase of the project relates to ship discharges – oil, ballast, bilge water and sewage and accidental spills. Likewise, the effects of anti-foul paints on bottom dwelling marine organisms, particularly clams and oysters, when the depth is relatively shallow and there are a number of crafts moored in the location can be significant. However, in this project anchorages are being provided only as safely measures and therefore, mooring of the ships for prolonged duration, that too in large numbers, is not envisaged.

The EMP prescribes the following:-

- All the ships transiting through the channel will comply with IMO Standards and follow MARPOL convention (MARPOL 73/78)
- Discharge of bilge, ballast, treated sewage, solid wastes, oily wastes and spillage of cargo will not be allowed.
- All the ships using the route will have proper treatment sewage will not be allowed to be discharged.
- Oil spill contingency plan will be drawn up by TPT with preparedness to prevent spread of spillage in GoM and Palk and its immediate recovery by deploying equipments and ships.
- The channel will be properly marked by navigation light buoys.
- Accidents due to collision will be averted through VTMS and also control of cruise speed.

Therefore, strict EMP will be in place to ensure that the ships transiting through the channel comply with the IMO standards, MARPOL 1973/78 and CPCB limits, if any.

(EIA report : pp.6.14 and 7.7 to 7.9)

Issues: 13. Rare fish species sea cow, sea turtle and dolphins will be affected.

Response: Presently, stray turtles and marine mammals suffer from propeller cuts, ghost fishing and death due to ingestion of jetsam and flotsam. Such instances may increase unless strict control is enforced in maintaining the channel pollution free and shipping speed is regulated. Such control has been provided in the EMP. EMP has further suggested posting of environmental watchers or well trained pilots aboard the transiting vessels to endeavour avoidance of injury to endangered species.

The proposed channel will have a depth of only 12m. Rare species may not, therefore, be affected by the channel.

It is of note that despite significant shipping activities, it has been reported that Olive Ridley turtles from the deep seas migrate to Gahirmatha beach in northern Orissa via Paradip Port for mass nesting during November-February every year. Reported mass killing of turtles in this region is primarily due to their getting entangled in gill netters and also due to poaching by local people for turtle flesh. This observation indicates that the proposed channel project may not have significant adverse impact on the migration and mass nesting of turtles.

(EIA report : pp.6.14 and 7.7 to 7.9)

Issues: 14. Non-availability of documents/reports by NEERI

Response: As the nodal agency, Tuticorin Port Trust had supplied sufficient copies of executive summary in Tamil and English and copy of EIA to all six Coastal District' Environment Engineers. The extract of EIA was also published in Port's website for several months. Detailed booklet were also supplied free of cost by the Port during public hearing containing salient features of the project, EIA and EMP.

Issues: 15. Sedimentation will occur in the canal during monsoon leading to heavy loss to the Govt.

Response: Computation of requisite maintenance dredging estimates is a major component of aby techno-economic feasibility study or EIA study, as a project of this nature involves significant dredging component. Maintenance dredging of about 0.1 million m3 per year is envisaged in the EIA study in the Adam's Bridge area and about 0.45 million m3 in Palk Bay area totaling 0.55 m3 for the channel. The studies carried out by the NSDRC indicate the region around Adam's Bridge as a significant sink for the littoral drift. In the case of extreme monsoon conditions and occurrence of cyclones in the GoM, such prolonged deposition of sediments may move north and enter Palk Bay through Pamban Pass and Adam's Bridge. Once the sediments enter the Palk Bay, environment conditions favour immediate deposition. This has been recognized in the EIA study. The quality of maintenance dredging required in this channel even in the worst case scenario will be far less than the quantity of annual maintenance dredging in ports such as Cochin, Kolkatta and a few others.

Issues: 16. During cyclone the channel will be unusable because of deposition of heavy silt.

Response: Information on the normal wave conditions is normally required for further studies on sedimentation and erosion and to establish the limiting conditions for navigation through the channel whereas information on the extreme wave conditions is required for the design of various structures like groynes and bank protection. The findings of the EIA study in this regard have been also duly verified with further modeling studies.

In terms of landfall, Andhra coast is the most vulnerable to the cyclones and Tamilnadu is third. Orissa is affected by the highest frequency of severe cyclones in October-November. In terms of storm surges, West Bengal coast is highly vulnerable, while Tamilnadu coast is vulnerable. Andhra and Orissa are the most vulnerable to coastal inundations. The fact that against the incidence of 61 cyclones on the Tamil Nadu coast during the period 1891-1995, only six had directly crossed the Palk Bay will convey that Palk Bay is less prone to incidence of cyclones than even the rest of Tamil Nadu. Even then the EIA states that in the case of incidents of cyclones in the Gulf of Mannar, due to conditions prevalent in Palk Bay there could be more sedimentation in the Palk Bay leading to increase in the quantity of maintenance dredging. However, the incidence of cyclones in the Gulf of Mannar because of its geomorphology is even less than in Palk Bay.

Issues: 17. The earlier alignment recommended by Screening Committee may be considered.

Response: The present alignment is considered based on the bathymetry to reduce the dredging distance of the canal and the dredge material. The alignment suggested by Steering Committee is passing near the Shingle Island which is only 12km. from the alignment whereas the present alignment is 20Km. away from Shingle Island and Marine Park.

Issues: 18. The project is not economically viable and sustainable.

Response: Economic Benefits

1. Qualifications
   - Savings in voyage time
   - Savings in fuel cost
2. Non Quantifiable
   - Increase in the level of economic activity in the region resulting in employment opportunities and revenue generation for the government. An illustrative list of activities includes ship repair facility, bunkering facility etc.
   - Multiplier effect due to investment in the channel i.e. being a development project, it will lead to manifold increase in the level of economic activity as a whole resulting in an overall increase in the level of economic activity due to multiplier effect.

- Possibility of coastal vessels plying on the coastal routes transport in cargo from/to the various ports in peninsular India.
- The channel will be strategic importance to the national defence agencies since the naval vessels can ply in territorial waters.

Economic Cost

Various associated social and environmental costs associated with the development of channel have been duly estimated.

Calculation of EIRR

The EIRR is calculated from the perspective of the government based on the following costs and benefits.

Costs

- Cost of the project – shadow rate of 90% of the capital cost (excluding interest during construction and other financing cost)
- Cost incurred for operation and maintenance of the channel including environment monitoring cost at the shadow rate of 90% (excluding interest and other financing charges)

Benefits

- Economic benefits on account of fuel saving
- Economic benefits on account of time saving

Issues: 19. The project will not be completed within 3 years definitely it will take 30 years.

Response: 77% of this work involves of dredging component. As the dredging technology is developed world-wide and as the work is going to be executed through global tenders, the period of 3 years for the completion of this project is adequate.

Issues: 20. This project will change the current pattern and that will have negative impact on fishing. Increase in Temperature. Increase in turbidity during construction will destruct fish species.

Response: A two dimensional (ocean) Model, DIVAST (Depth Integrated Velocity and Solute Transport) has been used for the hydrodynamic modeling. Current (tidal stream) measurements, with the assistance of the staff of Chief Hydrographic surveyor of India, were carried out at 10 locations in the study domain for spring tide conditions.

The special distributions of tidal currents have been modeled for two conditions.

- With the present bathymetry
- With the increase depths along the proposed alignment

The modelling study reveals that there will be no significant change in the current vectors due to dredging. The maximum current speeds is 0.7m/sec. The speed and directions are not changed significantly with geographical locations close to the proposed alignment. (EIA Report Aug 2004 P.6.15 to 6.18)

- The field investigations indicate no significant change in temperature.

Dredging of canal is proposed to employ modern technology; so turbidity will be within the prescribed limit.

Issues: 21. The mangroves will vanish due to implementation of this project. Dredging of channel will spoil mangroves in Muthupettai, Kodiyakarai and Athiramapattinam. Implementation of this project will destroy canal reef, algae sea breeds.

Response: The canal alignment is more than 30-40 Kms away from the coastal areas of Muthupettai, Kodiyakarai and Athiramapattinam. The dredged spoil is proposed to be disposed of in the Bay of Bengal at a depth of 25-30 mtr. There will not, therefore, be any damage to the Margroves during dredging of the canal.

Issues: 22. a. The dredged material will have an environment impact

b. Disposal of dredged spoil in the sea will alter the level of dissolved oxygen.

c. There will be environmental degradation.

Response:

1. The major activity during construction phase of project comprises capital dredging along the proposed alignment of the ship channel in Adam's Bridge and Palk Strait area. The area which requires intensive dredging to achieve depth of 12mtr. Across the Adam's Bridge area and in Palk Strait area. These areas have been studies for their actual bathymetry, seabed characteristics and hydrography. Sediment of different grain sizes mainly consist of sand, slit and clay.

2. The proposal envisaged by Ministry of Shipping was for creation of navigation channel to suit different draught requirement viz. 9.15, 10.7 and 12.8 requiring dredging depths of 10m, 12m and 14m respectively. For 12.8 m draught, channel width will be 500m whereas for 9.15 and 10.7 m draughts, channel width will be 300m. Based on hydrographic data collected by N HO it is observed that navigation depths in Palk Bay are restricted to about 12 m only. The total length from Adam's Bridge to Palk Strait is about 145 km. Based on the bathymetry data, requirements of dredging and quantity of dredge spoil likely to be generated have been computed for various options viz. 9.15m draught (10m deep), 10.7 m draught (12 m deep) and 12.6m draught (14m deept) channel with respective widths. It could be observed that quantity of dredged/spoil will increase with the depths to about 39, 82 and 313 million m³ respectively besides increase in length of channel to be dredged. In the event of proposal for 12.8 m draught requiring 14m depth, dredging will require to be carried out in entire Palk Bay area to create a channel of 500m width generating 313 million m³ of dredge spoil. Dredging all along the length of the channel in Palk Bay could be detrimental to ecologically sensitive area of this region. It would also involve heavy additional expenditure on dredging and disposal of dredge spoil. Thus, keeping in view environmental sensitivity and

economic viability the proposal for 14m depth 912.8 m draught was not even considered.

3. Though option for both 9.15m and 10.7 m draught were evaluated, study carried out by Shipping Corporation of India for estimating traffic potential at 7.9 and 11 draught recommended that a minimum draught of 10.7m be kept to make the channel viable. The proposed channel will have a bed width of 300m which will provide a sage width for a two way navigation channel.

4. The apprehension that the dredging of sea bed would result in increase of turbidity due to silt and clay both during drdging and disposal and that higher silt load in seawater would prevent penetration of sunlight in water body and may ultimately effect primary productivity has been expressed in the public hearing.

5. Primary productivity, the only means of synthesis of organic matter, is the basis of trophic web. Any damage to the lower trophic level would reflect into higher trophic including fish. If sunlight does not penetrate into the sea for days together, darkness would prevail on the bottom, which would adversely affect the photosynthetic activity of the symbiotic algae in the mollusks and corals. However this will happen only when turbidity near dredging and dumping locations would be beyond the prescribed level. In that event when silt gets deposited on all living organism especially on sedentary biota viz. pearl oysters, corals, algae, gorganids, other mollusks, annelids, prochordates, echinoderms, the egg mass of many free swimming animals, etc, they may get destroyed since these organisms have no/little locomotive power to move away from the dredging zone. Deposition of silt due to uncontrolled increase in turbidity due to dredging operations without a proper EMP may bury many small living organisms. Such slit may also enter into the gills of the animals and impair respiration . Slit also affects the planktonic life. Uncontrolled siltation affects the solubility of oxygen and gas exchange due to mineralization and pH changes and, thus, the amount of dissolved oxygen in the water may be reduced. Owing to the possible destruction of seagrass and seaweed beds due to turbidity beyond the prescribed levels for prolonged periods if dredging is done in an unscientific manner, larger animals such as dugongs, turtles and herbivorous fishes may also be affected. The dissolved components of the slit would enrich the algae growth and trigger the planktonic bloom. But this blooming may not be of much use since the benthic and other fauna, which mainly feed on them, are either not available or destroyed owing to silt deposition if dredging operations employ a technology which is inappropriate for the area.

6. The apprehension has also been expressed that whatever may be the method of dredging that is employed, a part of sediments removed from the sea

bottom would get spread to adjacent dredging area and that this would form as a mat and bury the entire fauna and flora into it. Adverse effects are also to be expected from uncontrolled and unmonitored pollution owing to the use of machinery for construction and operating units. Spillage of oil and grease, rust and metallic wastes due to wear and tear, marine litter, float including plastic bags, discarded articles could be the major pollutants.

7. The project authorities have taken great care to identify suitable dredging technology for this eco-sensitive region and to identify dumping locations after scientific modeling studies, to ensure that the turbidity levels in the dredging areas and dumping locations are within the prescribed limits, thereby eliminating altogether or minimizing to an insignificant level the possible impacts of dredging operations. To minimize impacts due to dredging and disposal of dredged material in this project, options for both land and sea disposal are considered in the EIA study based on environmental viability.

8. Disposal of dredged spoil generate during capital dredging containing sand is proposed to be done in sea in the proximity of dredging activity where potential adequate dilution and dispersion is available. It isobserved from the bathymetry data that a depth of 30-40 m is available about 25-30 Km. away from Adam's Bridge in GOM area. An exercise using dispersion modeling was carried out to study impact of dredged spoil on turbidity of sea water.

9. It has been inferred from these studies that the effect of the silty water when discharged will be localized and restricted to about 1500 mtr. From the discharge point. However, the plume will not surface immediately and the concentration of suspended solids in sea water will return to normal after 1500m in the line of advection.

10. As regards capital dredging envisaged in Palk Strait area this area ia close to Bay of Bengal where depth of more than 25m is available; disposal in the sea would be the preferred option.

11. As sand particles have discrete settling rise in turbidity of sea water in disposal locations is not envisaged thereby minimizing impact on primary production. In the event of disposal pf slit containing dredged spoil the turbidity zone will develop at the disposal will not allow   suspended solids plume to rise to surface immediately thereby providing adequate dilution before the plume surfaces in the direction of current. However, by the time the plume surfaces at about 1500m, concentration of suspended solids would return to background level.

12. The existing level of primary production in the project area will remain practically unaltered during the construction and operation phases of the ship channel. A proposal for disposal of silt/clay on land should be the more preferred option, though this is a costlier option and also contingent upon

availability of land and CRZ clearances. Even during sea disposal which is proposed now care would be taken to dispose of material well below the sea surface so that plume of suspended solids will remains submerged and will not cause alteration in surface turbidity and primary productivity. There would not be any significant change in water quality including turbidity due to the proposed deployment of trailor suction hopper dredgers for capital and maintenance dredging. Moreover, the envisaged dredging activities in the area are likely to cause much less turbidity than the international threshold, and thus the likely risk to marine biota is going to be minimal.

13. Disposal of sand (-30 million m^3) in the form of dredge spoil will temporarily alter the structure of benthos community. However, the benthos will restructure and recover to original status after capital dredging activity is completed.

14. Turbidity normally causes decrease in dissolved oxygen of the sea water. Since modern dredging technology will be employed for dredging, turbidity levels will be within the prescribed levels and, therefore, any decrease in dissolved oxygen will be transient and insignificant.

Issue: 23. Damage to fishing nets due to movement of ships

Response: The traffic management along the channel will be controlled by Tuticorin Port Trust. Movement of fishing boats and fishing nets will be watched by Tuticorin Port Trust to prevent any damage. If any damage occurs, necessary compensation will be given to fishermen through a committee which will be monitoring this as in the case of Tuticorin Port Trust.

Annexure 14

No. Z-12011/70/2003-IA-III
Government of India
Ministry of Environment & Forests
IA-III Section

Paryavaran Bhavan
CGO Complex, Lodhi Road,
New Delhi- 110 003
Dated the 2nd March, 2005

ORDER

Whereas, Ministry of Environment & Forests had received a proposal for environmental clearance for development of Sethusamudram Ship Canal Project (SSCP) from Ministry of Shipping vide their letter No. PD22012/96-PDZ(Pt.), dated 15.12.2003 to be implemented by M/s Tuticorin Port Trust.

And, whereas the said project attracts the provisions of the Environmental Impact Assessment Notification, 1994.

And, whereas, for the purpose of appraising the project under the provisions of Environmental Impact Assessment Notification, 1994 submission of public hearing report is mandatory.

And, whereas, this Ministry vide letter of even number dated 1.10.2004 had requested the Member Secretary, Tamil Nadu State Pollution Control Board to provide the public hearing report.

And, whereas, the Chairperson, Tamil Nadu State Pollution Control Board vide letter No. T11/TNPC B/28747/SSCP/2004-2, dated 21.10.2004 brought to the notice of Ministry of Environment & Forests that the public hearings were conducted in 6 coastal districts between 7th September, 2004 to 16th September, 2004 and that the public hearings remained incomplete and that the public hearing would be again conducted during 19th November to 30th November, 2004. It was also indicated that for this purpose the public notice has been issued in the local dailies on 10.10.2004.

And, whereas the Chairperson, Tamil Nadu Pollution Control Board was reminded on 25.11.2004 to send the proceedings of the public hearing to this Ministry.

And, whereas, the High Court of Madras in its Order dated 17.12.2004 in the Writ Petition Nos. 33528 and 34436 of 2004 and W.P.M.P. No. 40521 and 41570 of 2004 in the matter filed by Shri O. Fernandez, Co-convener, Coastal Action Network The Court whi8le upholding the prayer made in the Writ Petition N. 34436 of 2004 directed the concerned Authorities to complete the public hearing expeditiously if not already completed and send the reports with the minutes to the Ministry of Environment & Forests, Government of India forthwith. The Court further directed that further action to be taken forthwith by the Authorities concerned in accordance with law so that the Sethusamudram project be completed as expeditiously as possible.

And, whereas, till date this Ministry has not received the report of the public hearing conducted by the Tamil Nadu State Pollution Control Board.

Therefore, the Central Government in Exercise of powers conferred under Section 5 of the Environment (Protection) Act, 1986 hereby directs you to forward the public hearing proceedings within 7 days of issues of these directions, failing which the Central Government shall be constrained to evoke the provisions of Section 15 of the Environment (Protection) Act, 1986.

By order

Sd/-

(R. Chandra Mohan)

Joint Secretary to Government of India

To

Mrs. Girija Vaidyanathan

Chairperson,

Tamil Nadu State Pollution Control Board

76, Mount Salai, Guindy,

Chennai – 600032

Annexure 15

Lanka Accuses India of ignoring green concerns

Nidhi Sharma

Sethusamudram Shipping Canal Project (SSCP) seems to be leading India into a bigger international crisis. Despite India's tall claims that it is taking steps to preserve the ecological balance in Palk Strait, Sri Lanka has accused India of stalling the mechanism set up to address its environmental concerns.

Sri Lanka had raised serious environmental concerns in 2006 over the project, which envisages linking the Palk Strait with Gulf of Mannar between India and Sri Lanka through a canal. After this, India had set up a mechanism to address the concerns.

In the recently-concluded Winter Session of Parliament, Union Government gave a written reply that it is handling Sri Lanka's environmental concerns through a "mechanism for mutual discussion". The truth, however, is that India is brazenly undertaking the project without having any meetings or joint management plan with Sri Lanka.

The "mechanism" has not worked at all during 2007. Speaking to *The Pioneer*, Lanka Hydraulic Institute (LHI) director Malith Mendes said: "The 'mechanisms' are there, but it has been stalled for more than a year. There has been no response to Sri Lanka expert groups report of 2006. Meetings scheduled with Indian counterparts in 2007 were never held, presumably by lack of interest from India."

Mendes said that there have been several calls for a joint environmental impact assessment (EIA) "to which India has shown disregard or opposition". He said: "Sri Lanka can resort to provisions of the Convention on the law of the Sea to institute international legal action to safeguard its rights and interests. Sri Lanka should also propose a joint India-Sri Lanka Palk Strait Transnational Authority to handle affairs in the region. That is the way mature countries work."

At present, Palk Strait is shallow and this prevents large vessels from navigating through it. SSCP will dredge the sea bottom along India and Sri Lanka maritime boundary to a depth of 12 metres to enable larger ships to go through the Palk Strait. According to LHI studies, one the canal project is completed, it would increase the water flow in the region by two fold, especially during the monsoons. This would alter the temperature and salinity leading to ecological changes. At present, the region has 3,600 species of plants and animals, including Dugong, a marine mammal.

Sri Lanka had proposed that India should conduct a joint EIA study and ensure that the project does not have any ecological implications. To a question raised in Parliament, Union Shipping Minister TR Baalu gave a written reply in which he gave an assurance that all is well with Sri Lanka.

He said: "The Sethusamudram Shipping Canal Project is an Indian project and is located within the Indian side of the International Maritime Boundary Line. Certain issues have been raised by the Government of Sri Lanka, particularly on the environmental implications of the project. Consistent with the cordial and friendly relations between the two countries, the Government of India's endeavour is to address the genuine concerns of the Government of Sri Lanka through mutual discussion for which a mechanism has been put in place."

Annexure 16

Cong blames BJP for 'Ram Setu' project

In the face of a resurgent Sangh Parivar upping the ante on the Sethu Samudram ship canal project, demanding the scrapping of this "Ram Sethu" project the Congress today hit back, asserting that the current project was conceived, planned and cleared by the previous BJP-led NDA government during 1999-2004.

Seeking to turn the tables on the BJP, the AICC spokesman Mr. Abhishek Singhvi reeled off "hard facts and figures" to declare that the then Atal Behari Vajpayee government had envisaged the Sethu Samudram project as a "dream project" and approved it to get off the ground, which, he added, was only being taken forward by the present congress-led UPA government.

A day after the Sangh Parivar held in mammoth rally here to demand declaration of Ram Sethu off the Rameswaram coast as a "national heritage site", the Congress spokesman today said, "The rally was attended by senior BJP leaders who kept mum while their VHP and other Parivar counterparts kept raving and ranting against the project; it is a huge irony that the same BJP and its NDA allies, during their power at the Centre, had besides planning the project had actually even approved the present project alignment, number six, cutting through Adam's Bridge (Ram Sethu) in October 2002."

The Sangh Parivar has been up in arms against the Sethusamudram project off Tamil Nadu coast linking India with Sri Lanka, meant to facilitate the movement of ships from west to east coast of the country, because they feel it will cut through and damage the mythical Ram Sethu between the two countries that, they believe, was built by Lord Ram's simian warriors to reach the country of the demon king Ravan.

The Central government has maintained that the so-called Ram Sethu, also known as Adam's Bridge, is actually a natural geographical formation.

Referring to the NDA government's trackrecord on the Sethu project, Mr Singhvi traced a series of inter-ministerial consultations, the techno-economic-environmental studies by NEERI, the involvement of various ministers – including the then surface transport minister Mr Arun Jaitley, and the then shipping ministers Mr VP Goel and Mr Shatrughan Sinha, various announcements by senior leaders including Mr Vajpayee and Mr George Fernandes, during January 1999 to September 2003 to hold that "while planning and allocating budgetary funds for the project, the NDA regime never mentioned a single word about the so-called Ram Sethu. This highlights blatant lies and utter hyprocisy and double standards of the BJP."

Mr Singhvi also said that even the B JP's election manifesto for 2004 general elections mention its promise to execute the Sethu project.

The Congress accused the BJP of remembering Lord Ram only when the elections are round the corner. "The BJP always cynically remembers Ram only election time to politicize and communalise the situation, it has nothing to do with the true legacy of Ram, his truthfulness and his moral principles," charged Mr Singhvi.

In view of the sensitivity of the issue, the Congress itself shied away fro m taking any stand on whether it is in favour of the Sethu project or not, notwithstanding its DMK ally's passionate championing of it. To repeated questions in this regard. Mr. Singhvi had a standard reply: "The matter is now pending before the Supreme Court, we are not getting into the merits or demerits of the case, all documents and records have been submitted before the court, it is now for the apex court to decide."

To a question about the BJP's pitch to e xecute the project without damaging the Ram Sethu, Mr Singhvi said, "This is yet another hypocrisy and excuse by them, there is just no way you could execute the project without affecting the Adam's Bridge." He also added that the project envisages dredging of merely 300 mts out of the total 30,000 mts of Adam's Bridge.

Annexure 17

ALL-INDIA ANNA DRAVIDA MUNNETRA KAZHAGAM
HEAD OFFICE

226/275 Avvai Shanmugham Salai, Ropyapettah, Chennai – 600 014
Res.: "Veda Nilayam", 81/36, Poes Garden, Chennai – 600 086

J JAYALALITHAA
General Secretary, A.I.A.D.M.K.   Date 27-12-2007
Leader of Opposition,
Tamil Nadu Legislative Assembly

Dear Shri Ashok Singhal Ji

Right from the day the Rama Sethu Bridge demolition issue came into focus, I have been issuing statements pointing out how the destruction of the Bridge would be a grave threat to the environment, the flora and fauna of the region, apart from posing a very real danger of extinction to the marine life in the area, thereby seriously affecting the livelihood prospects of the fishing community for whom marine life is the only source of income. The historic and legendary association of the bridge with Lord Rama is deeply enshrined not only in the minds and hearts of the people of India but indeed in the minds and hearts of Hindus living all over the world.

Quite apart from the religious significance and historical importance of the Rama Sethu Bridge, and leaving aside the argument as to the origin of the Bridge, whether it is man-made or a natural formation, yet it is an undeniable truth that the Bridge is one of the wonders of the world and should be preserved for its value as a World Heritage Site. No government has the right to destroy this bridge, which is why my government refused to accord environmental clearance for the Sethu Samudram Canal project despite enormous pressure from the Central Government.

When the Union Government recently constituted a Committee to examine the project afresh before submitting a report to the Apex Court, I felt it was my duty to bring to the notice of the people the following facts:

This Committee can hardly be described as a committee of experts as is being claimed by the Union Government. At least three of the members are historians and they can only vouch for the historical validity of the Ram legend. One represents NEERI (National Environmental Engineering and Research Institute) which, being an interested party, is bound to have biased views. One member, R.S. Sharma, is a witness in the Ram Janmabhoomi case. Mr. S. Ramachandran, the Chairman of the

Committee, has already expressed his views publicly supporting the Sethusamudram Project. He cannot be expected to take a different or unbiased view now. All these facts hardly inspire any public confidence about the neutrality of the members of the Committee. More ominous is the fact that there are no social scientists to discuss the problems of the coastal people, particularly fishermen. To discuss navigational issues, there are no maritime or naval experts. There are no defence personnel to discuss security concerns, especially when the Sethu Samudram Canal becomes an international seaway. There are no oceanographers to discuss ocean currents and their effects especially as it comes within a Tsunami-hit area. There are no economists to discuss economy-related issues especially when the Sethusamudram Project is being touted as one that will economically uplift Tamil Nadu. These conspicuous and glaring omissions raise serious doubts about the credibility of the Committee and the possible veracity of its report.

While setting out the above facts, I made a demand that the Committee be disbanded.

In this context I had also pointed out that the Sethu Samudram Canal project as conceived would be of little use to the Nation, as it would have a centrifugal effect on the economy, navigational tonnage of ships, the environment and the sentiments of the widest sections of our people.

I had also filed a Writ Petition in the Supreme Court under Article 32 of the Constitution of India to protect the Rama Sethu, a structure of immeasurable historical, archaeological and heritage value from being destroyed, in the garb of carrying out an infrastructure project, on the following irrefutable facts.

Rama Sethu would fully qualify to be declared and protected as an ancient national monument, because it falls within each one of the parameters laid down in the definition of "ancient monument" in the 1958 Act.

The Rama Sethu, which is geographical terms is described in various survey maps and historical texts as "Adam's Bridge", by reason of its antiquity and unique features qualifies to be treated as World Heritage Site.

In a recent Satellite Image, NASA of the USA has spotted the Ancient Bridge and confirmed the physical existence of the bridge, which is a crucial structure of a bygone era, dating back millions of years and is estimated to be over 17,50,000 years old.

The bridge is of immeasurable sentimental value to millions of people in India and Hindus living all over the world and hence the structure is worthy of protection purely from a historical and archeological standpoint.

The Sethusamudram Ship Canal Project proposes to dredge the shallow ocean floor near the Dhanuskodi end of Rama's Bridge, to create enough leeway for ships to pass through the channel and will cut through the Bridge, thus damaging it.

International conventions have consolidated the solidarity of nations in preserving historical/archaeological sites and India, being a party to these conventions, is obliged to preserve heritage sites like the Rama Sethu.

Even during the Tsunami devastation the Rama Sethu Bridge acted as a natural barrier, preventing direct devastation, thus establishing its utility in the ecological/ geographical preservation of the area also.

I wish the rally to be held on 30.12.2007 in New Delhi by the Ramsethu Raksha Manch all success as it reflects the strong sentiments of the vast majority of the people of our Country.

With kind regards,

Yours sincerely,

Sd/-

J Jayalalithaa

To
Shri Ashok Singhal,
President,
Vishva Hindu Parishad,
Sector-6, Rama Krishna Puram,
New Delhi – 110 022
Fax No. 011 – 26195527, 26178992
e.mail – ashok.vhp@gmail.com

Annexure 17

Mishap hits dredging for Sethu Canal

The ambitious Sethusamudram Shipping Canal Project (SSCP) has ground to a halt after a 107-tonne dredging driller broke into two while cutting through Adam's Bridge, also known as Ramar Palam (Rama's bridge) off Rameshwaram coast, causing huge loss of money and time, according to an official of the Dredging Corporation of India, which is conducting the dredging of the seabed for the canal.

The official said the 'spud' or driller of the Holland-built Cutter-Suction-Dredger (CSD) Aquarius broke as it could not tackle the hard bottom of the Adam's Bridge. One piece of the spud was recovered from seabed by a floating crane and the other piece was likely to be retrieved on Wednesday, he said.

He said a tem from IHC, the Holland company that had made the driller, was expected on Wednesday to assess the damage and explore the possibility of welding the broken pieces together for reuse. The welding work could be done at the Kochi shipyard. "This is a major setback and the cost could be heavy in terms of money and time loss, particularly if the IHC recommends total replacement instead of repairing the spud," said the official who did not want to be named.

The Rs. 2,400 crore Sethu project is already embroiled in a legal wrangle with a local RSS leader and some other Hindu associates moving the court at Ramanathapuram, having jurisdiction over the project site, seeking to halt the dredging as it would destroy the Ramar Palam, the bridge built by Lord Rama for crossing to Lanka to rescue Sita from Ravana. The petitioners have demanded that Ramar Palam, spotted by the NASA satellites, should be preserved as a monument.

Taking on file the civil suit from the Hindu leader, the Ramnad court has issued notices to the Union Government, the SSCP, the Archaeological Survey of India and the district collector. The case is coming up for hearing on February 5.

Several environmentalists too have objected to the Sethu projct fearing it would cause irreparable damage to the delicate marine biodiversity in the region. The project envisages dredging the seabed in the shallow waters of the Palk Strait and Palk Bay to create a navigation lane for ship: to sail from India's western coast to the east without having to circumnavigate Sri Lanka. The dredging work had begun in July 2005.

Annexure 18

'SSCP can only handle small ships'

The Sethusamudram Shipping Canal Project (SSCP) has been designed in such a way that on ly ships below 40,000 dead weight tonnage (SWT) can sail through it, said K. Chidambaram, president Institute of Marine Engineers (India). "All other ships have to take the route circumnavigating Sri Lanka", said Mr. Chidambaram here on Tuesday, reacting to the recent controversy over chief of naval staff admiral Sureesh Mehta's statement that only small ships will be able to sail through the SSCP. Union minister for shipping, road transport and highways TR Baalu had later questioned the veracity of the chief of naval staff's statements.

Mr. Chidambaram, a qualified marine engineer from the Directorate of Marine Engineering and Technology (DMET), said that each canal was designed and built with certain capacity. "The SSCP is meant for small ships and one need not feel sorry about airing its capacity," he said.

Mr. Chidambaram also talked about the World Shipping Forum 2008, a three-day international conference, organised by the Institute of Marine Engineers in the city from Thursday. "Shipping experts, and marine engineers will present papers on the different aspects in the shipping industry. The theme of this years' conference will be strategies for future shipping challenges." Said Mr. Chidambaram.

World Shipping Forum is a quadrennial event that attracts ship owners, business strategists and policy makers.

Experts like Km. Laubstiebn of the World Maritime Univeristy Sweden, D.T. Joseph, former secretary, shipping, industry. S. Hajara, President of the Indian National Ship Owners Association and Vijay Shankar of the Group will attend the forum.

Mr. Chidambaram described the Institute of Marine Engineers as a body of more than 9,000 professional marine engineers.

Annexure 19

JANATA PARTY

A-77, Nizamuddin (East)
New Delhi – 110013, India
February 13, 2008

Ms. Pratibha Patil
President of India
Rashtrapati Bhavan
New Delhi.

Dear Maniniya Pratibhaji

As you may know, I have filed a PIL on the Setu Samudram Channel Project (SSCP) which is being heard in the Supreme Court, wherein I have already secured an injunction order against damaging the Rama Setu. However, since the PIL is non –adversorial in nature therefore I am always available to assist the Government to find an amicable way out that meets the aspirations of the people as well attains the goals of the Project.

Ever since the DMK Government filed an affidavit in the Supreme Court on the Jallikattu matter stating that the Supreme Court ought to reverse its earlier order because religious and public sentiments would be hurt by a strict application of the laws on prevention of animal cruelty, the Government's case for demolition of the Rama Setu in order to implement the SSCP, stands null and void. Hence it hardly matters any more whether Rama Setu is man-made or natural formation because a billion Hindus plus those who wish Hindus well, would be offended deeply and hurt by any damage to the Rama Setu.

In this connection I enclose with this letter a copy of the statement issued by Hazrat Maulana Jamil Ahmed Ilyasi, President of the All India Organizations of Imams of Mosques (Regd.), opposing the demolition or damage to the Rama Setu precisely on this basis. The statement was published by leading Hindi newspapers, cuttings of which are enclosed with this letter. The same sentiments have also been expressed by the President of the Republic of Croatia in a letter to Paramhans Swami Maheshwarananda (enclosed). Therefore, while investigations may continue by the ASI in association with GSI and other independent experts about the horacity of the Rama Setu, and whether it qualifies to be a national heritage and ancient monument, it is now a settled question that following the Jallikattu decision of the

Supreme Court that Rama Setu cannot be touched because it will cause an explosive upheaval amongst the billion Hindus in India and outside.

It was good to meet you and explain in detail the issues so that as good democrats we can find an amicable way out of the present impasse. I urge you to call for the papers and ask the government not to waste any more public funds on this project. Instead, the Ministry of Railways may be asked by the PM to construct a double line broad gauge rail connection along the eastern coastline from Tuticorin to Kolkata, and also that the government build a container port at Tuticorin. This project will be cheaper and more development intensive than the SSCP.

Best Regards,

Yours sincerely,

Sd/-

(Subramanian Swamy)

All India Organisation of Imams of Mosques (Regd.)

A representative body of half million Imams of India

HAZRAT MAULANA JAMEEL AHMED ILYASI
(President)

Date : 17/1/08

प्रकाशनार्थ

अखिल भारतीय इमाम संगठन के राष्ट्रीय महामंत्री मौलाना उमेर इलियासी ने तमिलनाडू मुस्लिम मुनेत्र कडगम द्वारा आदम सेतु को तोड़े जाने की कड़ी निंदा की है। पिछले दिनों चेन्नई में तमिलनाडू मुस्लिम मुनेत्र कडगम के महासचिव टी. अली ने कहा था कि आदम सेतु सभी मुसलमानों के लिए जियारत की जगह है, परंतु मानव हित में इसे तोड़े जाने से मुसलमानों को कोई एतराज नहीं है।

मौलाना इलियासी ने इस पर कड़ी आपत्ति जताते हुए कहा कि उपरोक्त तंजीम इस बात को भूल गई है कि देश का हित इस सेतू को बचाने में है तोड़ने में नहीं। उन्होंने कहा कि केरल का सारा तटीय क्षेत्र सुनामी की चपेट में आ सकता है, इस सेतु को तोड़ने से तमिलनाडू के तटीय क्षेत्रों का थोरियम भंडार नष्ट हो जाएगा मछुआरे बेरोजगार हो जाएंगे जिसमें मुसलमान मछुआरे बहुत बड़ी संख्या में हैं। सेतु के टूटने पर वनस्पतियां नष्ट हो जाएंगी और सबसे बढ़कर इस क्षेत्र के अंतर्राष्ट्रीय जल क्षेत्र बनने से यह अमेरिका और चीन के षडयंत्रों का अड्डा बन जाएगा।

मौलाना इलियासी ने आगाह करते हुए कहा कि रामेश्वरम स्थित यह एकमात्र ऐसा सेतु है जिसकी रक्षा के लिए देश के हिंदू, मुसलमान और ईसाई एकजुट हैं। यह सेतु मुस्लिम के लिए भी उतना पवित्र है जितना हिंदुओं के लिए, ऐसी हालत में तमिलनाडू

मुस्लिम मुनेत्र कडगम सेतु को तोड़ने की वकालत करके देश हित में नहीं बल्कि तोड़ने के लिए पर्दे के पीछे से काम कर रही विदेशी शक्तियों के एजेंट के तौर पर कार्य कर रही है।

मौलाना इलियासी ने इस बात पर खुशी जाहिर की है कि तमिलनाडू के ज्यादातर मुसलमानों तंजीम की इस अपील को नकार दिया है। मौलाना इलियासी ने देश के लोगों को आश्वस्त किया कि इस देश के मुसलमान भी सेतु की रक्षा के लिए एकजुट हैं।

मौलाना अब्दुल रज्जाक

प्रेस सचिव

आदम सेतु तोड़ने की निंदा

अखिल भरतीय इमाम संगठन के महामंत्री मौलाना उमर इलियासी ने तमिल मुस्लिम मुनेत्र कडगम द्वारा आदम सेतु तोड़ने की निन्दा की है। संगठन ने टीएमकेडी के महासचिव टी. अली के उस ब्यान पर आपत्ति जतायी है जिसमें उन्होंने सेतु को मानव हित में तोड़ने पर सहमति जतायी है। मौलाना इलियासी ने कहा है कि पुल को तोड़ने में नहीं यथास्थिति बनाये रखने में ही लाभ है।

रामसेतु बचाने आगे आया इमाम संगठन

नई दिल्ली, जासं : अखिल भारतीय इमाम संगठन भी रामसेतु को तोड़े जाने के विरोध में सामने आ गया है। संगठन ने रामसेतु को आदम सेतु बताते हुए इसकी रक्षा किए जाने की मांग की है। संगठन ने कहा कि सेतु को तोड़ना देशहित में नहीं है। इमाम संगठन के राष्ट्रीय महामंत्री मौलाना उमेर इलियासी ने कहा कि रामेश्वरम स्थित आदम सेतु एक ऐसा सेतु है, जिसकी रक्षा के लिए देश के हिंदु, मुसलमान और ईसाई एकजुट हैं।

यह सेतु मुसलमानों के लिए भी उतना ही पवित्र है, जितना हिंदुओं के लिए, ऐसे में मुस्लिम मुनेत्र कड़गम के महासचिव टी. अली ने आदम सेतु को तोड़े जाने की वकालत कर देशहित में कार्य नहीं

किया है। उन्होंने आरोप लगाया कि इस जरह की बातें करने के पीछे विदेशी ताकतों का हाथ है। तमिलनाडू की अधिकतर मुस्लिम संस्थाओं ने इस जरह की अपीलों को नकारा है।

श्री इलियासी ने कहा कि आदम सेतु को तोड़े जाने से केरल का तटीय क्षेत्र सुनामी की चपेट में आ सकता है। साथ ही तमिलनाडू के तटीय क्षेत्रों का थोरियम भंडार भी नष्ट हो सकता है, वहीं हजारों मछुआरे बेरोजगार हो जाएंगे और वनस्पतियां नष्ट हो जाएंगी। यह अंतरराष्ट्रीय जल क्षेत्र बनने से अमेरिका और चीन के षडयंत्र का अड्डा बन सकता है।

His Holiness
Paramhans Swami Maheshwarananda

Your Holiness, honored Swamiji,

Thank you for the book of the holy epic poem Ramayana which you gave to me during our meeting.

My attention was especially drawn to the chapter about the bridge between India and Sri Lanka, the bridge which is hidden in the depths of the sea. Although invisible to our eyes (but not to NASA Satellites) the bridge is a part of world and human heritage and this is why The Republic of Croatia is also fighting to protect its underwater heritage because, in doing so, we are preserving our roots. The bridge is a witness of Ramayana, the story about good and evil, a universal story, but also an individual story, about the struggle of a hero, an individual, but also of a nation, which to me, both as a president and an individual, is very interesting reading material. It makes me think about myself, about my roles of a statesman who could help You with your efforts.

I therefore support the proposal that Ram Setu should be protected from devastation and put on the UNESCO World Heritage list.

I will use this opportunity to thank you once again for visiting Zagreb and for the seminars and devoted efforts to spread peace, tolerance, understanding, and conscien ce about the preservation of our planet Earth.

Sincerely

The President of the Republic of Croatia
Stjepan Mesic

MAJULI RE-NOMINATED FOR HERITAGE STATUS

The Majuli Island—the largest fresh water mid-river deltaic island in the world—in Assam's Jorhat district has been re-nominated by the government for the World Heritage List in the "Cultural Landscape" category in 2008.

The decision to approach the UNESCO with a fresh nomination was taken on the Prim e Minister Manmohan Singh's intervention. To address the issues raised by the UN body he convened a meeting with Tourism and Culture Minister Ambika Soni and Water Resources Minister Saifuddin Soz last October.

After the first nomination in 2004, the International Council of Monuments and Sites—an advisory body to the UNESCO World Heritage Centre—carried out an evaluation of the island in 2005. Based on its report, the World Heritage Committee sought information of the mapping of "Sattras" and their influence, an inventory of the cultural resources of the Sattra, an analysis of their condition, and preparation of a risk preparedness strategy.

After India supplied the information, the committee, at its Luthuania session in 2006, decided to refer the nomination back for collating and providing more information. The Archaeological Survey of India, nodal agency for nomination of Indian sites on the World Heritage List, submitted a detailed document.

Given the complexity of the site, the additional documentation was prepared adopting a multidisciplinary approach in consultation with field agencies under the Ministry of Water Resources and the Assam government.

The island is formed at the confluence of the Brahmaputra and Lohit rivers. The island witnesses floods, erosion and siltation, and has a fragile eco-system. The World Heritage Committee will meet in Canada in July to decide the island's status.

Annexure 20

V. Sundaram IAS
Chairman, Tuticorin Port Trust   1ˢᵗ July, 1982

Dear Sri Lakshminarayanan,

Government of India appointed a Committee under your Chairmanship to examine the economic feasibility of the Sethu Samudram Shiping Canal Project last year. I had the great privilege of serving as a Member of this Committee. We have had several rounds of useful discussions both in New Delhi and in Tuticorin. The Committee also visited Rameshwaram and the adjoining relevant areas in Ramanathapuram District. The Committee had made arrangements for organized public hearing sessions in Rameshwaram, Ramanathapuram, Madurai and Tuticorin to ascertain the views of the public on the proposed Sethu Samudram Project. Several organisations representing trade and commercial interests, maritime and fishing interests and cultural and religious organisations representing Hindu interests placed their considered views before the Committee.

As I am reverting back to the Government of Tamil Nadu on completion of my tenure as the first Chairman of the Tuticorin Port Trust on the 8ᵗʰ of July 1982, I wanted to invite your specific and particular attention to the following recommendations of the Sir A. Ramaswamy Mudaliar Committee made in 1956 :

The recommendations were that a canal should be aligned through Mandapam to create a land-based canal like the Panama or Suez Canal. Sir A Ramaswamy Mudaliar specifically warned that any idea of cutting a channel passage through the Adam's Bridge (that is, Rama Sethu or Setubandha) SHOULD BE ABANDONED. To quote from Sir A Ramaswamy Mudaliar Committee Report (1956):

"We are convinced that the Adam's Bridge site is unsuitable for the following reasons:

"*Firstly*: The shifting Sandbanks in this area present a far more formidable problem – both at the stage of construction and during maintenance – than the sand dunes on the island site".

"*Secondly*: The approaches to a channel would be far too open with no possibility of construction of protective works. A channel at this site – even if it can be made and maintained (which is unlikely) – would entail definite navigational hazard".

"*Thirdly*: The channel would be bordering on the Setusamudram Medial Line".

"In these circumstances we have no doubt, whatever that the junction between the two sea should be effected by a Canal; and the idea of cutting a passage in the sea through Adam's Bridge should be abandoned".

You might recall that representatives from several Hindu organisations like the VHP, RSS, and some Vaishnavite organisations from Srirangam gave a representation to the Committee, making it clear in strong and unequivocal terms that the Ramar Sethu Bridge, held sacred by all the Hindus of India from times immemorial, should on no account be damaged or destroyed during the construction of the planed Sethu Samudram Canal. All of them invited our attention to the above recommendations of the Sir A Ramaswamy Mudaliar Committee in 1956 and also to the Report of Sri R. Natarajan IAS in 1968. According to both these Reports, Ramar Sethu Bridge should on no account be damaged or destroyed. Both Sir A Ramaswamy Mudaliar and Sri R. Natarajan had proposed such alignments as would leave the Ramar Sethu Bridge untouched. I request you to stick to this rigid and fixed position while finalizing your Report.

I am rather concerned about the surreptitious subterranean efforts being made by the Catholic Church in Tamil Nadu to influence the Government of India to somehow destroy the Ramar Sethu Bridge just in order to give a death blow to an ancient symbol of Hindu religion held sacred by millions of Hindus in India and abroad. I am fully aware of these moves because prior to my joining Tuticorin New Port as its Administrator on 1st of June 1978, I had worked as the District Collector and Magistrate of Tirunelveli District and during that period the District Police had brought to my personal attention the Herculean and nefarious efforts of the Church to resort to all devious methods and means as part of an organized programme of evangelization and proselytism in the Southern Districts of Tamil Nadu in general and Tirunelveli District in particular.

Throughout the period of British rule, the Government showed a sensitive concern towards symbols and places of worship of the Hindus, Muslims and Christians without any discrimination. Only after independence under the chimera of secularism, Government and Governmental agencies have become insensitive towards the feelings of the Hindu population in India as a whole. To illustrate this point, I am enclosing the copy of a very interesting letter which was sent by Lord Pentland, Governor of Madras (1912 – 1919) in March 1914 to Lord Hardinge, the then Viceroy of India which speaks for itself (Please see Annexure I).

I request you to treat this as my ʻ*Note of Dissent*ʼ in my capacity as a Member of the Sethu Samudram Committee. I am marking a copy of this letter to Sri Mohinder Singh, Secretary to the Government of India in the Ministry of Shipping and Transport for information and necessary action.

With warm regards,

Yours sincerely,

Sd/- V. Sundaram.

To
Sri Lakshminarayanan
Development Advisor (PORTS)
Union Ministry of Shipping and Transport
Transport Bhavan, Parliament Street
New Delhi.

Copy to:
Sri Mohinder Singh
Secretary to the Government of India
Union Ministry of Shipping and Transport
Transport Bhavan, Parliament Street
New Delhi

- On finalisation of the alignment, Techno-economic viability studies were carried out covering traffic, economics and benefits. It is understood that the progress report is basically meant for finalising the Channel alignment paving way for further studies.

Annexure 21

Lord Pentland was Governor of Madras from 1912 to 1919. He visited Rameshwaram in 1914 when Sir Alexander Tottenham (1873–1946) was the District Collector of Ramanathapuram. Lord Pentland was so overwhelmed by what he saw in Rameshwaram that he wrote as follows to Lord Hardinge, the then Viceroy of India:

'For me Rameshwaram, very much like India as a whole is the real world. We English men live in a mad house of abstractions. Vital life in Rameshwaram has not yet withdrawn into the capsule of the head. It is the whole body that lives. No wonder the English man feels dreamlike: the complete life of Rameshwaram is something of which he merely dreams... I did not see an English man in India who really lived there. They are all living in England, that is, in a sort of bottle filled with English air... History can be events or memory of events... along the Bay of Bengal the Madras Presidency runs, with the well-governed city of Madras at its center and the sublime and glorious temples of Tanjore, Tiruchi, Madurai and Rameshwaram adorning its Southern boundaries. And then Adam's Bridge – a reef of sunken islands' beckons a\us across the Palk Straits to Ceylon, where civilization flourished more than 2000 years ago... Linga stones may be seen in many places on the highways in my Presidency. Hindus break upon them the coconuts which they are about to offer in sacrifice. Usually the phallic ritual is simple and becoming; it consists in anointing the stone with consecrated water or oil, and decorating it with leaves. At the Rameshwaram temple, the Linga stone is daily washed with Ganga water, which is afterwards sold to the pious, as holy water or mesmerized water has been sold in Europe. All these are a little part of my beloved Presidency – indeed my favourite India. Right from the dawn of history, India is extraordinarily discontinuous... from early times in India, it is ethnology, philology, and archaeology much can be expected. I would earnestly request you to direct the Archaeological Survey of India (ASI) to undertake an extensive and intensive survey of Rameshwaram and its beautiful environs, particularly with reference to the historic and primordial Adam's Bridge'.

1st July, 1982

Sd/- V. Sundaram
Chairman, Turicorin Port Trust

Index